The Talking Turtle

And Other Ozark Folk Tales

The Talking Turtle

And Other Ozark Folk Tales

Collected by Vance Randolph

With Notes by Herbert Halpert

Illustrations by Glen Rounds

Columbia University Press, New York, 1957

TO MARY CELESTIA PARLER

PREFACE

PARTS OF this collection were first published in *Western Folklore*, the *Southern Folklore Quarterly*, and *Midwest Folklore*. A few items are reprinted from my books *Ozark Mountain Folks* and *From an Ozark Holler*, issued by the Vanguard Press in 1932 and 1933, both long out of print. Others appeared in two pamphlets, *Funny Stories from Arkansas* and *Funny Stories about Hillbillies*, published by E. Haldeman-Julius in 1943 and 1944. I thank the owners of these copyrights for permission to use the material here.

V. R.

Eureka Springs, Ark.

CONTENTS

INTRODUCTION

THE OZARK Mountain people are without material wealth, but they have inherited a leisurely way of life. There is still time for conversation, and Ozark speech is unhurried and reminiscent. Hillfolk love to tell of minor marvels past, and little things are long remembered. Every hilltop has its tradition, every hollow is full of tales and legends. The people do not read much. Their stories are shaped and polished by the hazards of oral transmission. Some of these tales derive from clans or families rather than individuals, and many were known to the great-grandparents of the present generation. That doesn't matter at all, because novelty is not important in a frontier culture. One never hears an Ozark humorist say, "Stop me, if you've heard this one."

I first visited the Ozark country more than fifty years ago. Since 1920 I have lived here practically all the time. I rode around the country with horse traders, interviewed old settlers, married Ozark women, cultivated country editors, and shacked up with berry-pickers under the ledges. It was a great opportunity, and a privilege, to hear the stories that my neighbors told. I wrote down hundreds of these yarns, and sold a lot of humorous dialogue to cartoonists and gagwriters. Those boys probably think I invented the stuff, but I never made up a hillbilly wisecrack in my life. It was just a matter of recording the talk I heard in lonely cabins and crossroads stores, beside little campfires on the gravel bars, at drinking parties and dances and other backwoods frolics.

At one time I had an assistant who set down every word in shorthand, like a court reporter. Later I used a phonographic recorder in collecting folksongs, and this machine served well enough for stories. More often, when neither stenographer nor recorder was available, I made notes in pencil to be typed a few hours later, while the details were still fresh. Whatever the method, my intention was to record each tale as accurately as possible, without any polishing or embellishment. I have not combined different versions of a tale, or used material from more than one informant in the same story, or tried to improve the storyteller's style. I cut out some cusswords, because the profanity which strengthens oral fiction soon grows monotonous in print. Several of my informants, knowing that their speech was being recorded, made a conscious effort to avoid obscene words and phrases. This expurgation was their idea, not mine. My feeling is that a "vulgar" story cannot be cleaned up without spoiling it.

In recording folksongs, rhymes, riddles, dance calls, or other material which is learned by heart, it is essential that every word be set down exactly as the informant says it. I believe that a literal rendering is less important in the case of folktales. I have obtained phonograph records of the same individual telling the same story, sometimes after an interval of several months. A comparison of these recordings shows a considerable variation in the words used by the narrator, while the quoted speech of the characters in the tale is usually unchanged. So it is with my transcriptions.

I have tried to retain the Ozark idiom, but if one sets down the hillman's exact words his peculiarities of speech appear to be exaggerated. The common query, "Whereabouts do you-uns live at?" fits the speaker's mouth perfectly and sounds all right on a phonograph record, but it looks too thick in print. So I generally write, "Whereabouts do you live?" or "Where do you-uns live?" or "Where do you live at?" All three of these forms are heard in the Ozark country, and they are easier to read than what the man actually said. It doesn't seem worth while to emphasize dialect by respelling words. The local-color novelists used to write *keer* for care, *mout* for might, *shore* for sure, *hit* for it, *ax* for ask, *idy* for idea, *sartin* for certain, *heathern* for heathen, *mixtry* for mixture, and so forth. There is no denying that many hillfolk favor such provincial or archaic pronunciations. But this is a book of tales, not a dissertation on the Ozark phonology. Oral narratives are hard to bring off in any case, because the timing is often fouled up in type; written sentences fail to reproduce the significant pauses and rhythms. The use of a heavy dialect adds to the difficulty.

In selecting the material for this book there has been no effort to please the sophisticated or literary taste. I have not chosen items of special interest to historians or folklorists. The tales printed here are not the most sensational pieces in my collection, and many of the stories which appeal to me personally have been omitted. I believe that such a sampling should be representative, rather than handpicked for any particular group of readers, if one is to present a true picture of the storytelling tradition. These tales, therefore, are those which the narrators themselves like best, and tell oftenest.

Some of the stories are no more than fragments of local history, village legends, or fence-corner anecdotes. Others are genuine *Märchen,* with roots deep in European soil. I have little knowledge of their provenience, but my friend Herbert Halpert, familiar with the details of folktale scholarship, has supplied annotations and references to international parallels. Dr. Halpert's notes, in the back of the book, are addressed primarily to professional folklorists. But they are of great interest to me, and I believe they will appeal to other amateurs.

This collection is full of pleasant memories for me, because the persons who told the tales were my friends and neighbors. It was in 1899 that I met Price Paine, a Cowskin River fisherman; he was the first storyteller I ever knew, and one of the best. Another old-timer was Darby Hicks, who traveled all over the world but never lost his taste for Ozark corn. Leo McKellops, a physician with a fund of fantastic stories, was my friend for many years. Mary Elizabeth Mahnkey made a great impression on me, and so did Otto Ernest Rayburn, and Wythe Bishop, and Ern Long, the one-armed poker player. I remember Jean Lightfoot, and Fay Stubbs, and Ann Miller, and Callista O'Neill who lived on Bear Creek. There was another pretty girl who told me some sprightly tales, but she married a preacher by way of penance, and wouldn't want her name mentioned here. George Hastings contributed some good yarns from his students at the University of Arkansas, and "Skip" Hazlewood came through with a garland of lusty anecdotes. Many of these people are dead now, but they were unforgettable men and women, all born storytellers. I wish that their several skills could be conjured up for those who read the printed pages.

V. R.

The Talking Turtle

And Other Ozark Folk Tales

THE TALKING TURTLE

ONE TIME there was a fellow named Lissenbee, and the trouble was that he couldn't keep nothing to himself. Whenever anybody done something that wasn't right, Lissenbee would run and blab it all over town. He didn't tell no lies, he just told the truth, and that's what made it so bad. Because all the people believed whatever Lissenbee said, and there wasn't no way a fellow could laugh it off.

If he seen one of the county officers going to a woman's house when her husband was not home, Lissenbee would tell it right in front of the courthouse, and so there would be hell to pay in two families. Or maybe some citizens liked to play a little poker in the livery barn, but there wasn't no way to keep it quiet, on account of that goddam Lissenbee. And when the Baptist preacher brought some whiskey home, there was Lissenbee a-hollering before the preacher could get the keg out of his buggy. After while the boys was afraid to swipe a watermelon, for fear old blabbermouth Lissenbee would tell everybody who done it.

The last straw was the time Lissenbee found a turtle in the road. It was bigger than the common kind, so he stopped to look at it. The old turtle winked its red eyes, and it says, "Lissenbee, you talk too damn much." Lissenbee jumped four foot high, and then just stood there with his mouth a-hanging open. He looked all round, but there wasn't anybody in sight. "It must be my ears have went back on me!" says he. "Everybody knows terrapins is dumb." The old turtle winked its red eyes again. "Lissenbee, you talk too damn much," says the turtle. With that Lissenbee spun round like a top, and then he lit out for town.

When Lissenbee come to the tavern and told the people about the turtle that could talk, they just laughed in his face. "You come with me," says he, "and I'll show you!" So the whole crowd went along, but when they got there the old turtle didn't say a word. It looked just like any other turtle, only bigger than the common kind. The people was mad because they had walked away out there in the hot sun for nothing, so they kicked Lissenbee into the ditch and went back to town. Pretty soon Lissenbee set up, and the old turtle winked its red eyes. "Didn't I tell you?" says the turtle. "You talk too damn much."

Some people around here say the whole thing was a joke, because it ain't possible for a turtle to talk. They claim some fellow must have hid in the bushes and throwed his voice, so it just sounded like the turtle was a-talking. Everybody knows

4

that these medicine-show doctors can make a wooden dummy talk good enough to fool most anybody. There was a boy here in town that tried to learn how out of a book, but he never done no good at it. The folks never found nobody in these parts that could throw his voice like that.

Well, no matter if it was a joke or not, the story sure fixed old blabbermouth Lissenbee. The folks just laughed at his tales after that, and they would say he better go talk to the turtles about it.

BLOOD IN THE CELLAR

ONE TIME there was a woman getting supper for her man, and she thought he would come in from the field pretty soon, so she was in a big hurry. The woman told the little girl to go down cellar and fetch some potatoes. She went down the steep stairs into the dark cellar. It seemed like the stairs was steeper than common, and the cellar was all black only one place right by the 'tater pile, where a little thin light come in.

When she got to the light place, the little girl seen a big clot of blood. It was laying on the bare ground, because they didn't have any floor in the cellar. And then come a voice right out of the 'tater pile, "If you tell your mother about my blood, I'll come and *get* you!" The little girl was scared, so she run back up the steps and told her mother. But the woman says, "Nonsense!" And then she says, "Go straight down cellar and get the 'taters, like I told you."

So the little girl went down the steep stairs again, and it seemed like they was getting steeper all the time. The cellar got darker all the time too, only at one place. When she come to the light spot by the 'tater pile, the blood was still laying there, with a head grown onto one end of it. And then come the voice again, "If you tell your mother about my head, I'll come and *get* you!" The little girl was scared, so she run back up the stairs. "It's got a head now, and it said the same thing!" she told her mother. But the woman says, "Nonsense!" And then she says, "Go and get the 'taters, or I will whip you within a inch of your life."

So the little girl went back down cellar, and it seemed like the steps was steeper than ever. The cellar got darker, too, only at one place. When she come to the light spot by the 'tater pile the head was still there, with a great big body grown onto it. "Pick up your 'taters," says the voice, "but if you tell your mother about my body, I'll come and *get* you!" The little girl looked at the thing pretty careful, and she kind of got over being scared, so she says, "All right." She took the potatoes up the steps, and didn't tell her mother nothing. The woman just cooked the 'taters for supper, and thought no more about it.

That night after the little girl was in bed and the house all dark, she heard big strong steps a-coming across the room. And then a big hand touched her, but it didn't hurt, and she never said nothing. Pretty soon the voice says, "If you had told your mother about my body, I'd have come and *got* you." The little girl was kind of used to the thing by now, and she wasn't scared a bit.

The sun come up mighty fine next morning, with birds a-singing and all. The little girl just kind of grinned, and never said a word about the thing that scared her, or what happened in the night. Some folks thought maybe she seen the

6

thing pretty often after that, and there was all kind of stories a-going round. But the little girl never said nothing, and nobody ever did know for sure.

THE CURSE OF MONEGAW

ONE TIME there was a big bunch of Osages lived in Missouri, and their chief was named Monegaw. He was a rich Indian, that had lots of silver. Some think he got hold of a treasure that the Spaniards hid somewhere. That's how they come to call him Monegaw, because it means "rich man" in the Osage language. Anyhow he was pretty well off, a-trading silver for ponies and guns and powder and all kind of things. Monegaw had four wives, and they was the prettiest girls for miles around. A Indian that had money always got the best women, just like the white folks do nowadays.

Old Monegaw did not have nothing against the white people when they first come, but pretty soon he seen they was no good, and it looked like they would ruin everything. The Osages was great hunters, and did not do no farming, except the women planted a little corn down by the river. Sometimes they would raise a few beans and squashes. The Indians did not believe in cutting down trees and plowing up the ground. They knowed it would make floods, and spoil the whole goddam country. But them white people did not believe it, because they figured the Osages was ignorant and superstitious. So pretty soon the whole bunch got to fighting, and a lot of folks was killed on both sides.

The white people shot squaws and children just the same

as men, because they said nits make lice. And they took scalps and counted coups just like the Indians did, so there was hell to pay generally. But finally a lot of soldiers come, and when the Osages jumped on them there was a big battle. Them soldiers was trained to fight and they had better guns, so the Indians did not do no good. Pretty near half of the Osages got killed, and the rest of them left Missouri. They went out West somewheres, because there wasn't no white men out West in them days.

Everybody figured that Chief Monegaw would go along with the tribe, but he never done it. He says it ain't right for a man to go traipsing round the country at his age, so he just hid out in the big timber. No white man ever seen him alive after that. But one day some bear hunters found him laying dead in a cave, all dressed up in the finest Osage clothes you ever seen. One of the hunters had knowed him in the early days, before the trouble. So they wrapped old Monegaw in a red blanket, and buried him on the bluff beside the river.

After while the white people built a town there on account of the sulphur water, and they called it Monegaw Springs. They had several big houses, and a fine log hotel, and it was quite a settlement. People come there from all over the country, because they thought sulphur water would cure diseases. They used to drink the water and bathe in it, but the tourists claimed it never done no good, and some of them wanted their money back. The old-timers always said the town wouldn't amount to nothing, because old Monegaw had put a curse on it. And sure enough, when the War Between the States broke out, some Yankee bushwhackers killed more people than the Osages ever done, and burnt all them big houses plumb to the ground.

The springs are still there, of course, but the town is mostly gone now because the doctors say sulphur water can't cure nothing, so people don't believe in it no more. The tourists stay away, because the ticks and chiggers are so bad. Folks laugh at such as that nowadays, but the early settlers always figured that Chief Monegaw throwed a spell on the whole place. Maybe there ain't nothing to them old tales, but Monegaw Springs is a hard-luck country, all right. If you don't believe it, just go up there along about August, and wrastle with them ticks and chiggers awhile.

THE FOREIGNER'S HEAD

ONE TIME there was an old couple lived south of Forsyth, and they was pretty well fixed. The old man kept the money in a strong iron box with a big padlock on it. Him and his wife was real old-timers, both of 'em tougher than a boot. They wasn't scared of robbers nor nobody else.

The old folks was setting out in front when two young fellows come along the road. They looked like foreigners, but the old man asked them to eat supper anyhow. Pretty soon they begun to talk about money, but the old man had his six-shooter where he could get it easy, and he didn't worry none. After while the two young fellows got mad at each other, and one says, "Come outside. I don't want to make no trouble in these people's house." So they both got up, and one pulled out a big knife and cut the other's head right off. The old folks just set still, but the old man had the pistol in his hand. Him and the old woman never turned a hair. They had seen people killed before, and who gives a damn about foreigners, anyhow?

9

But the man which his head was cut off didn't fall down like a dead man ought to. He stood right up like anybody else. The head rolled across the path. Then come a voice, and it says, "Pick me up." The man without no head reached down and began to fumble around. "Over here, you fool!" says the voice. "Under the rosebush." So the fellow felt in under the rosebush and picked up his head. "Put me back where I belong," says the head, and the young fellow done it. The head turned round a couple of times, and wagged up and down. "That's fine," says the young fellow. Pretty soon he took a red handkerchief and wiped the blood off his neck.

The old folks never did remember what happened next. But when they come to theirself it was plumb dark. When the old woman lit the lamp, she seen that the foreigners was gone. The money was gone too, and the iron box laid open, with the key in the padlock. The old man hitched up and went for the sheriff, but it didn't do no good. The sheriff come out there, but he couldn't see no blood on the ground, so how could anybody have got their head cut off? The sheriff says, "You must have dreamed it, and maybe you never did have no money anyhow." He says, "What do you mean, to fetch me away out here for nothing?" and then the sheriff got in his buggy and went back to town.

The old folks never did find out what become of them two foreigners, and they never did get their money back, neither. The fellow that wrote a piece in the paper about it, he thought the old folks must have been hypnotized. There ain't no doubt but what them foreigners got control of the old folks' mind some way, to make 'em think they seen a fellow put his head back on like that. Maybe a lot of things people call hypnotizing is just the same as witches done in the olden times. The

10

old man says he never did believe in witches before, but now he don't know what to think.

BIG WIND AT HURLEY

ONE TIME there was a bad cyclone come through Hurley, up on Spring Creek. Hurley was quite a settlement in them days, with a big gristmill, and more than two hundred people was a-living there. When the storm struck it tore down a lot of houses, and scared the hell out of everybody in town. That was the time Jack Short got hit on the head with a stick of wood, and it pretty near killed him.

A fellow named Alec Hood was coming across his pasture when things begun to turn black. He seen the cloud, and started to run for the creek bank, but he never made it. The wind lifted him clear up over the treetops. Joey Jones run out of the grocery to see what was going on, and quick as a wink he was sucked up in the air too. There was horses, and woodsheds, and turkeys, and even haystacks a-flying along beside him. Them two fellows was whirled round and round, and once they passed so close that they shook hands. "Goodbye, brother," says Alec, and Joey just nodded because he was plumb breathless. It looked like they was both gone goslings for sure.

Everything turned out all right, though. The wind kind of slowed up after while, and finally they come down in a field about three miles from home. Neither one of 'em was hurt a bit. The folks sure was surprised to see them boys, when they come a-walking into town.

There ain't no doubt about them being blowed up in the

air, just like they said. There was plenty of folks that seen 'em a-flying over the trees. But maybe the part about shaking hands and saying "Goodbye, brother!" was made up. The neighbors never did hear nothing about it till several years after the cyclone. It was Alec that told the tale, down at the crossroads store. Joey Jones just grinned, and wagged his head. He never did deny it, though. And everybody knows that funny things do happen sometimes, when one of them big winds hits a settlement like Hurley.

THE WELL DIGGER

ONE TIME there was a fellow named Buck Price, that was digging a well out in the pasture. When he went to work one morning he seen where the bank had caved in, so the hole was half full of rocks and dirt. Buck hung his hat and coat on the fence same as always, but everything looked mighty discouraging, and he didn't feel like working anyhow. Pretty soon he throwed the pick and shovel under some bushes. Just then the Starbuck boys come along with a jug, and so they all went a-fishing over on Big Piney.

The sun was about two hours high when one of the neighbors come through the pasture, a-looking for a colt. There was Buck's hat and coat on the fence, and no tools in sight, so he figured Buck must be under the cave-in. Pretty soon guns was a-firing and horns blowing all over the neighborhood, just like somebody's house was afire. Buck's woman was hollering louder'n a steam whistle, because she thought poor Buck was dead, sure. Folks come a-running to see what was the matter, and they all began to throw rocks and dirt out of the well.

With everybody working together that way, it wasn't no time till they cleaned out the hole, but they didn't find no corpse. Pretty soon a boy stumbled onto the pick and shovel, where Buck had throwed them under the bushes. The folks didn't know what to think. Most of the neighbors went back home, soon as they found out for sure that Buck wasn't in the well. Some of them was pretty mad, but they didn't say much.

After while here come Buck a-walking up the lane. Him and the Starbucks had drunk the jug plumb dry, and he had a nice string of catfish. Buck was feeling pretty good, and when they told him about what happened he laughed like a fool. "It sure was neighborly of them boys to clean out my well," says he. "I reckon it would have took me a week to get all them rocks out by myself."

Most of the folks never opened their mouth, but they figured that Buck must have hid out a-purpose, just to fool the neighbors into doing all that work for him. Everybody knows a fellow like Buck Price don't go fishing without his hat on, unless there's some special reason for it.

LOOSENING WEEDS

ONE TIME there was a couple from Kansas City come down to make a float trip on the James River. They was going to float five days, and camp out on the gravel bars at night. Frank Pine had a new johnboat and a lot of good stories, so these Kansas City folks hired him to guide

13

'em. Frank knowed the river as well as anybody. But the fellows that run the float trips didn't like to send him out, because he was always playing jokes on the tourists.

Everything went along fine for two or three days, and they caught some nice bass. Then the woman looked like she didn't feel good, and the man says, "We will have to go back, because my wife needs a physic and I forgot to bring the goddam pills." Frank told him don't worry about that because the woods is full of pure vegetable remedies, much better than them drugs they sell in town. So he went and dug some mayapple root, and boiled it down to a good thick ooze with a little sugar. And the woman from Kansas City drunk a whole cupful.

Everybody knows that mayapple root is the strongest loosening weed there is, and the dose Frank give that woman was enough to physic two horses. Right after supper she was took with a terrible bellyache. Then she busted out of the tent and run for the brush. The poor woman kept a-trotting back and forth all night, and Frank just laid there. When morning come she was still going strong, so Frank and the man went fishing, but the woman had to stay in camp all day. She was up most of the next night too, and the man says, "My wife has got the worst diarrhea I ever seen, and it must be something she ate." Frank says, "maybe she took a little too much loosening weed. But all's well that ends well," says he. So the man laughed and says, "I reckon you're right." The woman just looked at Frank, but she didn't say nothing. So then they got on the train and went back home, and Frank told all the boys what a fine joke he played on the woman from Kansas City.

Next summer the couple from Kansas City showed up

14

again, and the fellow that run the float trip tried to send them out with Charley Barnes. But the woman wanted the same man they had last year, because she says he's the best guide on the river, and they wouldn't trust theirself with nobody else. So the fellow that run the float trip went and got Frank Pine, but he says for God's sake don't play no jokes on them people this time. And Frank says all right.

The first day out they all felt fine, and the woman was chewing gum so she gave Frank some too. They eat a lot of roasting ears for supper, and Frank had to get up twice in the night. Next day they didn't catch no fish, but the woman didn't care; her and Frank just kept a-chattering and chewing their gum all day. That night poor Frank had to get up four times, and next morning he had the backdoor trots so bad he couldn't eat no breakfast. Every few minutes he had to stop the boat and go to the brush. And that's the way it was from then on. The last day of the float the woman from Kansas City was feeling fine, and she kept on a-chattering. But poor Frank was so weak he couldn't hardly paddle the boat. He just set there a-chewing his gum, and looking miserable.

When they got back to the boat landing the man from Kansas City give Frank five dollars extra, and he said him and his wife sure had a good time. And the woman from Kansas City shook hands with Frank, and give him a whole box of chewing-gum. Frank says, "Thank you," and grinned at them the best he could. But soon as they drove off he went home, and set in the privy all day Sunday.

About the middle of the week Frank's little girl says, "Pappy, can I have some of your medicine?" and she held up the box with the chewing-gum in it. Frank told her the stuff was just gum, but she says it is Feen-O-Chew, that city folks

15

use nowadays instead of Epsom salts. It didn't sound sensible to Frank, because he never heard of Feen-O-Chew. He hunted up his specs, and studied the letters on the box very careful; after while he went down town and showed it to the fellow that run the drugstore.

When Frank come out of the drugstore he throwed the box in the ditch, and never said nothing to nobody. The story got out some way, though, and poor Frank never did hear the last of it. He didn't play no more jokes on people from Kansas City, neither.

THE WICKED STEPMOTHER

ONE TIME there was a man lived on the highway, and his wife died. He had a little boy and a little girl. Pretty soon a good-looking woman come along, and she told the folks she loves children better than anything else in the world. So the man married her, because he wanted somebody to make a home for his kids. Everything went along fine for awhile, and then the woman got awful tired of the little girl.

Finally the man and the little boy went out hunting, and the woman told the little girl to bring some milk from the springhouse. "If you spill one drop," she says, "I'll cut your head right off!" When the girl come back the woman wanted to know if she spilled any milk, and the little girl says no. But that was a lie, because she did spill some. The woman asked her three times, and finally the little girl says yes. "Go and fetch me that block," says the woman. But the little girl wouldn't do it, and she says, "No, you would cut my head off."

So the woman went and got the block herself, and held the girl down on the block. Then she took the axe and cut the little girl's head right off.

The woman carried the corpse out in the woods and threw it in a deep cave. But when she come back after the little girl's head, she seen her husband and his boy coming home. So she put the head in a sack right quick, and hid it under the boy's bed. The boy says, "Where is my sister?" but the woman told him the little girl is upstairs.

After while they went to bed, but the boy didn't get no sleep. He could hear his sister's voice say, "Stepmother cut my head off! Stepmother cut my head off!" She just kept saying it over and over, all night long. Next morning the boy told his father, and the man looked under the bed. Sure enough, there was the little girl's head in a sack.

The man says to his wife, "Go get that block, and fetch me the axe." But the woman says, "No, you would cut my head off." The man told her three times, so finally she had to do it. He held the woman down on the block, and then he took the axe and cut her head right off. It served the wicked stepmother right, and that is the end of the story.

BLIND DATE ON BULL CREEK

ONE TIME there was a young fellow come down from Kansas City, and he kept talking about the pretty girls back home. He says things is kind of slow down here, because there ain't no girls to run around with of a night. The boys got tired after while, and they didn't want to hear no more about it. So finally they told the young fellow that the prettiest girl in the county lives up on Bull Creek, and she would like to have a date with him. But it will have to be done mighty quiet, because Irene's pappy thinks she ain't old enough to be running around with boys yet.

The young fellow just laughed, and smoothed his hair back. "Who cares what her pappy thinks?" says he. "If they're big enough, they're old enough, is what I always say. Just show me where she lives!" So that night the boys took him out to a cabin on the Bull Creek road. The house had been empty for years, but they hung a lace curtain in the window and lit a lamp inside, so it looked like somebody was living there. The boys told the young fellow to watch out for the girl's pappy, but he just laughed some more. "Cornfed gals is my special meat," he says. "If anybody gets in the way, I will bust him with these here brass knucks. That's the way we do in Kansas City," says he.

The boys went back up the road, and the young fellow walked in the front gate. He whistled a couple of times, but didn't get no answer. So then he scratched on the front door. "It's me, Irene," he says. "Come on out." Just then something moved in the bushes by the well house, and he heard two little clicks. *Ba*-LOOM! says an old shotgun, and blowed fire and smoke all over the place. The young fellow give one big jump, and tore down a whole panel of fence. *Ba*-LOOM! come the second barrel, and he took right out through the timber. The gun was just loaded with dried peas, but the young fellow thought it was buckshot a-whistling all round him. "Don't shoot!" he yelled, but the brush was still a-crackling over to the right. The young fellow figured the girl's pappy must be reloading on the run, a-trying to cut across ahead of him. So he turned to the left, and slid down a steep bank, and waded

18

the creek up to his elbows. Everything was quiet after that, but the fellow from Kansas City didn't take no chances. He run till he was plumb wore out, then laid up under a ledge and shivered all night. It was pretty near daylight before he got back to the hotel.

Along in the afternoon the young fellow come down to the poolhall. The home folks kind of grinned at him, but nobody mentioned his date with the farmer's daughter. After while some of the boys started singing a song about Irene the village queen that was sweet sixteen and how she played on her accordeen, but they didn't get no rise out of the young fellow from Kansas City. He must have suspicioned, by this time, that the whole thing was a put-up job.

Anyhow, he was always pretty close-mouthed after that. And if anybody says anything about the cornfed gals on Bull Creek, the young fellow just let on like he didn't hear a word they said. He never done no more bragging about all them pretty girls he had went with back in Kansas City, neither.

THE HOLLERING STORY

ONE TIME there was a farmer lived on a high ridge above Sugar Creek, and another fellow lived on the bluff right across the valley. They was pretty near a mile apart, but they used to holler back and forth anyhow. It's surprising how far you can hear people that way, if they go slow and kind of drag their words out. When them two fellows got to hollering, everybody that came along the road listened to what they said, and the boys down at the store used to tell a lot of jokes about it.

19

The man that lived on the bluff hollered across one morning, and he was trying to borrow a plow. The ridgerunner didn't want to lend his plow, so he hollered back, "The hi-i-i-ired ma-a-a-an bu-u-u-usted it." The fellow that lived on the bluff drawed a good breath, and then he says, "Sa-a-a-ame one got your dau-au-au-aughter in tro-ou-ou-ouble?" Pretty soon the answer come back, "Ye-ea-ea-eah, sa-a-a-ame feller." So the the first man hollered, "Re-e-e-eckless son-of-a-bitch, ai-ai-ai-ain't he?" The folks down in the valley all laughed like fools, when they heard that.

After while the fellow on the ridge started hollering again. "Sa-a-a-ay, did you tell Jim Henson I was a li-i-i-iar?" And the fellow that lived on the bluff answered back, "No-o-o-o, he must have fou-ou-ou-ound out from so-o-o-omebody e-e-e-else."

The boys down at the store used to make fun of them two fellows a-hollering back and forth, but most of the tales about it was just made-up jokes, and maybe never really happened that way at all. Pretty near all of them hollering stories is full of dirty words anyhow, and not fittin' to be wrote down in no book.

IT JUST SUITS ME

ONE TIME there was four fellows went deer hunting down in the Kiamichi Mountains, which is in Oklahoma. They pitched a nice camp with two tents, and then cut cards to see who done the cooking. Whoever turns the low card has got to cook for seven days. But if anybody kicks about the grub the cook just pulls off his apron, and the fellow that kicked has got to do the cooking. It is an old-time rule that all them deer-hunters go by, except a few city fellows that chip in and hire a regular cook.

Well, Doc Henley drawed the trey of clubs, and he fixed 'em a pretty good supper. But next morning they didn't get nothing but big yellow biscuits that was burnt on the bottom and raw on top, and the coffee tasted like Doc must have put bitter-weed in it. The boys made a terrible bad face, and Harmon Kelley pretended like he was going to puke. But they was all careful not to say one word about the victuals, so Doc had to go ahead with his cooking.

They didn't get no deer yet, but Doc served up a fine dish of sidemeat and boiled turnips for supper. There was good coffee too, and some fair-to-middling cornbread, with a big platter of fried eggs. The boys didn't say much, but they eat every scrap of them victuals, and helped Doc wash up the dishes. Then they all played seven-up, and told stories, and passed the jug around. Everybody went to bed a-feeling fine. Doc felt pretty good too, only he was goddam tired of cooking.

Next day the boys killed two fine bucks, and so they all got pretty drunk by supper-time. Doc served up four big slices of deer liver. Three of them was fine, but the biggest slice of all was rubbed plumb full of salt. Harmon Kelley grabbed it, and stuck a piece in his mouth. He chawed away for a minute, and then spit it right out on the ground. "Good God, that stuff's salty—but it *just suits me!*" he says. The other boys all laughed like fools, and Doc pulled off his apron. Harmon claimed he liked liver good and salty, but the boys

21

made him do the cooking for two days anyhow. And then it set in to raining, and everybody had got a deer by that time, so they broke camp and went back home.

The boys told the story around town, and the folks thought it was a good joke. So Harmon Kelley's saying got to be kind of a byword. People used to say it whenever they got hold of something that wasn't much good. Like one time a country boy married a no-account schoolmarm down in the south end of the county. She was a Methodist, and a loose woman besides. He wouldn't never have married her, only they got him so drunk he didn't rightly know what was a-going on. When the kinfolks come to see 'em next day, the fellow says, "Well, it was kind of sudden, but Mabel *just suits me!*" That kind of talk sounds kind of funny to a stranger, maybe. But the home folks knowed what he meant, all right.

THE BIG BLACK BOOGER

ONE TIME there was an old gentleman, and he used to tell stories to his grandchildren at night. Some of them tales scared the children so bad they couldn't go to sleep. There was one about a man that cursed and swore and went fishing on Sunday, and he was very immoral about other things too. This wicked fellow was alone in his cabin one night, and he was setting by the fireplace. All of a sudden there was a noise inside the chimney, and down come two big black feet.

The feet was fastened onto little black shins, and the wicked man just set there a-goggling at them, so scared he couldn't move a muscle. Next come down two big black knees,

22

and a big black body like a barrel, and two great wide shoulders, and two big strong arms, with hands bigger than hams. The wicked fellow was shaking like a leaf by this time. At last a big round head come down, with long teeth, and its eyes a-shining like two coals of fire. And then the big black booger just stood there on the hearth, the awfullest sight anybody ever seen in this world or the next.

The wicked man was scared pretty near to death by now, but he finally spoke up, "Wh-wh-who are you?" The big black booger just showed its teeth, and spit out fire. "You'll find out," it says.

Pretty soon the wicked fellow says, "What makes your feet so big?" And the big black booger answered, "Walking up and down the earth."

After while the wicked sinner spoke up again, "What makes your shins so little?" And the big black booger groaned, "Decayed and gone with time."

Next the wicked man says, "What makes your shoulders so wide?" And the big black booger answered, "Carrying wood and coal, to keep the hot fires a-going."

The poor sinner thought about this, and then he asked, "What makes your head so round?" And the big black booger told him, "Thinking, planning, and plotting."

The wicked man just shivered a minute. "Wh-wh-who are you, Mister?" says he. "And what do you want here?" The big black booger just wiggled its fingers, and grinned like a wolf. "I am the Devil," it says, "and I'm *after you!*"

When the old gentleman come to this part of the story he always roared out "I'm *after you!*" loud as he could, and give a big jump like he was going to grab somebody. The kids all yelled at the top of their voices, too, because it scared the living daylights out of them. So then their mother would come running in, and she says, "Listen, Paw, you mustn't tell no more of them scary tales, because the children can't go to sleep!" The old grandfather just laughed, and that's all there is to the story.

BIG FRAID AND
LITTLE FRAID

ONE TIME there was an old man, and he didn't like the young fellow that was coming to see his daughter. So he figured a way to scare the young fellow plumb out of the country. The old man dressed up in a sheet to look like a ghost, and then he went out in the woods. He set down on a log to wait till the young fellow come along.

Maybe the scheme would have worked, only they had a

pet monkey that used to be with a medicine-show. The monkey dressed up in a pillow slip and followed right along behind the old man. The moon was shining bright, and pretty soon the young fellow come a-whistling down the path. The old man flopped his sheet, and give a couple of loud groans. So then the monkey flopped his pillow slip, and he give a couple of screeches. The old man turned around and seen the monkey, and it looked like a sure enough ghost. He give a yell and took out for the house, with the monkey right close behind him. The monkey squalled like it was scared, too.

The young fellow just stood there beside the path. He seen the whole thing, and it tickled him pretty near to death. "Run, big Fraid, or little Fraid will ketch you!" he hollered. And then the young fellow laughed so loud you could hear him plumb to the house.

The old man kind of give up trying to scare folks after that, and says he don't want to hear no more about it. So then the young fellow and the girl went right ahead with their sparking, same as always. After while they got married, and lived happy ever after.

THE WISE MAN'S QUESTIONS

ONE TIME there was two brothers by the name of Mooney, and they was both twins. They looked just alike, except one of them was named Joe and the other's name was Jack. But even folks that knowed their names by heart couldn't make out which was which, without asking them. And even then you couldn't tell for sure, because them boys was the worst liars in the whole country.

The old folks used to laugh about the time a wise man up

on Beaver Creek wanted to hire a boy to help him, and learn the trade. Joe Mooney says, "What does a wise man have to do?" The folks told him a wise man just sets in a nice cool cave, and people come and give him silver money, so then he advises them how to run their business. "That's just the kind of a job I want," says Joe, and then he went over to see about it.

The wise man says well, it depends on whether he can answer three questions. The first question is, "How many leaves is on that big sycamore tree?" The second question is, "Who was the first man in the world?" And the third question is, "What am I thinking this minute?" If a boy can't answer them three questions he ain't smart enough to learn the trade, so there ain't no use talking about it. Joe Mooney says he can't give the answers now, but he will go home and study, and next morning he will answer them questions easy. So the wise man says all right.

When Joe got back home he says to Jack, "Well, it looks like I won't get the job, because nobody could answer them fool questions." But Jack says never mind, I am smarter than you, and I can tell him the right answer. "Hell," says Joe, "that won't do no good, because it's me that wants to learn the trade." Jack says, "Don't let that worry you, because we look just alike and the wise man can't tell the difference. Soon as I answer the questions I'll come back home, and you can go over and take my place." So Joe says all right.

Next morning Jack went over to Beaver Creek, and the wise man says, "Well, how many leaves is on that big sycamore tree?" And Jack answered, "Thirty-two thousand, four hundred and fifty-seven. And if you don't believe it, you can count 'em yourself." So then the wise man says, "Well, who

26

was the first man in the world?" And Jack answered, "George Washington was the first man, but if you're going to count foreigners it was Adam." So then the wise man says, "Well, what am I thinking this minute?" And Jack answered, "You think you're a-talking to Joe Mooney. But it ain't so, because I am Jack Mooney which is his twin brother."

The wise man just laughed. "The job's yourn," says he, "and it don't make no difference what your name is. Wise men don't have no names, because names is no more than scratches in the dusty road." And so one of the Mooney boys went ahead and learned the trade, and he done pretty good at it. Some say it was Joe that turned out to be a wise man, but maybe it was Jack. There was considerable talk about it, but the folks never did find out for sure.

FIDDLER'S CAVE

ONE TIME there was a girl named Jenny who fell in love with a fiddler, and so she went to all the dances. They used to give most of the dances in a cave. It had a big room right in front, with a wide entrance. The floor was clay, tromped down smooth and hard as rock. That cave was a fine place to dance on hot nights, and young folks come from all over the country. It was a big cave that run back under the mountain for miles, with underground rivers and black lakes and a big pour-off called Faralone Falls. The boys would walk back in the dark sometimes, to take a drink out of their jug. But the nice girls always stayed in the front room of the cave, where the light was.

Jenny's folks didn't want her to run around with the

fiddler on account of his wild and swearing ways, and he didn't have no money anyhow. So finally she promised to marry another man, a good steady farmer that had hogs on the range and three good cows in his barn. Him and Jenny went to the dance that night. The fiddler seen how things was and he felt mighty sick, but he didn't say nothing. After while he got another fellow to fiddle in his place, and walked back into the cave. Everybody seen him go, with his fiddle in one hand and a big old jug in the other.

The folks never thought much about it right then, and they all went on a-dancing. But when the dance broke up it was pretty near daylight, and the fiddler didn't show up. His friends knowed he was feeling pretty bad about Jenny, so they figured he must have got drunker than common and just laid down somewheres to sleep it off. A couple of banjo-pickers got a lantern and went back into the cave to look for the fiddler, but they couldn't find him nowhere.

About noon some of the neighbors come over, and they searched the whole cave plumb back to Faralone Falls. Them people carried torches and lanterns all over the place, and took turns a-hollering. The fiddler didn't make no answer, but every once in a while they could hear fiddle-music. Sometimes it sounded right close up, and other times so far off you couldn't hardly hear it. The folks hunted that fiddler for three days, and they all heard them fiddle-tunes, mighty low and lonesome. On the third morning it sounded kind of muffled and ripply, like the fiddle was under water. Finally there come a kind of guggling noise, like a jug filling up in the spring. And after that everything was still as the grave, so the folks all give up and went home.

The fiddler never did show up, but everybody thought there

28

was something funny about it, and they never had no more dances in the cave. Some people say that if you go by the entrance on a hot night, when there ain't no wind, you can hear fiddle-music to this day. But maybe it's just one of them old stories, without no truth in it. They still call the place Fiddler's Cave, though. Lots of folks just hurry on past, because it's kind of spooky around there of a night.

THE HOLY ROLLERS

ONE TIME there was a bunch of Holy Rollers at a place called Protem, which is in Missouri but pretty close to the Arkansas line. The folks down that way go kind of hog-wild about religion every year, soon as they get the corn laid by, and some of 'em built a brush arbor right beside the new highway. The Holy Rollers always had their meetings in that arbor, and you could hear 'em hollering and jabbering all night. Everybody knowed there was scandalous doings at them meetings, sometimes. But the Holy Rollers was a kind of trashy lot anyhow, so the home folks didn't pay 'em no mind.

It was different with the tourists, though. Them city people that heard the racket always wanted to go and watch the Holy Rollers roll. One night a bunch of fishermen from Springfield walked into the arbor, just as a great big fat gal got religion over in a corner. So out she come a-shouting, and right up the aisle she went. She was jumping and kicking and whooping and hollering every breath. When she got to the pulpit that gal give one last yell, and throwed herself face down on the dirt floor. She fell so hard that her dress flew clear up over her head, and she wasn't wearing much in the way of underclothes, neither. "Praise the Lord!" hollered the preacher, and then he just stood there a-looking down at her.

One of the fishermen was kind of a gentleman, and he didn't think it was right for a woman to expose herself that way be-

fore all them people. So he walked over where she was laying and started to pull down her dress. "Don't do that, brother!" says the preacher. "Don't pull her dress down. Just let her lay like Jesus flang her!"

The city fellow was considerable set back, but he done like the preacher said. They just left the big fat gal a-laying where she was throwed by the Power. Holy Rollers have got some mighty peculiar notions. Them fishermen laughed about it all the way back to camp.

A LITTLE MORE CIDER

ONE TIME there was a fellow had a fine big apple orchard, and soon as the new highway come through he got to selling apples in baskets. He built a little wooden stand down by the road, so pretty near every automobile that come along would stop. Then the fellow got hold of a cider-mill, and after that he sold cider in bottles, with a nice label on it. Finally he fixed up a icebox in the stand, so as to sell cider by the drink. The tourists liked it fine, and the fellow was making pretty good money.

A big bunch of people from St. Louis come along one day, so him and his wife was both down at the stand, and their little boy was a-leaning against the counter. The little boy was about six years old, and he was a cute little fellow. So a big fat tourist women says, "Sonny, do you like cider?" The boy smiled at her. "Oh yes, ma'am!" says he. The tourist woman laid down another dime and passed the boy a full glass, but the little fellow kind of held back. "Go ahead and drink it," says the tourist woman.

She kept on a-urging him, but the little boy just shook his head. "We got our own cider in the cellar to drink," he says. "This here selling-cider is made out of apples which has got worms in 'em." The tourist woman set her glass right down on the counter, and the other customers didn't drink no more cider, neither. They just looked at each other kind of funny

31

for a minute. Then they all walked out to their big shiny automobiles and drove off down the road.

The fellow and his wife just stood there goggle-eyed till the customers was plumb out of sight. Pretty soon the man cut a switch and tanned the little boy's behind all the way back to the house. He sure laid it on heavy, and you could hear that boy a-hollering clear down to the crossroads.

The old mother-in-law got pretty mad, and she says things has come to a pretty pass when a young-un gets a whipping for telling the truth. The fellow says it ain't so. "I raise my children to be honest," says he. "Why, if Tommy was to tell them tourists that the cider *ain't* made out of wormy apples, I'd give him a licking for lyin'."

The old woman studied awhile. "You whip him if he says the apples is wormy, and then whip him again if he says they ain't! It don't make no sense to me. What are you-uns tryin' to learn that boy, anyhow?"

The fellow just kind of grinned at her. "We're tryin' to learn him to keep his mouth shut," says he.

THE SPANISH BURIAL

ONE TIME there was a settlement where the boys always played jokes on newcomers. They didn't mean no harm by it. If a man come to town that the folks didn't like, everybody just let him alone. But if he was a good fellow, they'd get him out in the woods to hunt snipes, or something like that. Sometimes they would make out like some pretty girl was crazy about him, and when he went to her house they'd run him off with blank cartridges, and maybe grease the footlog besides. Just get some of the old folks to tell you about Walter Crabtree, that come down from St. Louis to run the stave-mill. He hadn't been here a month till the boys pulled the old "Spanish Burial" joke on him.

The way it started, a fellow come running in to tell Walter that Rob Ramsay is dead all of a sudden, and they have got him laid out in the room back of the store. Walter felt pretty bad about it, because him and Rob Ramsay was good friends. So he run over to the store, without stopping to put on his coat even. There was Rob laying in a coffin, and they had put white stuff on his face so he looked like a corpse. Walter just stood there, and you could see he was all broke up.

There was a wide blue ribbon across Rob's chest, and a big brass badge. Doc Owens says it is a medal Rob got in the war, but the letters on the badge is so fine nobody can't make them out. Then he says Mister Crabtree has got good eyes, and maybe he can read it. So Walter bent down close, and just then Rob reached up and grabbed him round the neck. Walter yelled like a steam whistle, but Rob held on. The other boys snatched up wooden slats and begun to paddle Walter from behind. Things was mighty lively for a minute, and then Rob got to laughing so hard he had to turn Walter loose.

Walter Crabtree just looked from one of them fellows to another. He was breathing pretty hard at first, but pretty soon he grinned. "Well, boys," says he, "the joke's on me, and so are the drinks." So they all went over to the tavern, and it wasn't long till Walter was laughing loud as anybody. But he says the next time somebody dies in this town, he is going to stick his knife in the corpse's belly, just to make sure the son-of-a-bitch is dead! Walter wasn't really mad, because it was like being initiated into a lodge. He knowed the boys didn't mean no harm, and they was all good friends after that.

TO HELL WITH JOPLIN

ONE TIME old Milt Wilson took some hogs to Joplin, and after the hogs was sold he went to the hotel. They give him a fine room, and there was a good saloon right in the same building. The people in the diningroom was kind of stuck-up, and Milt didn't like the looks of it. So he walked down the street and et his supper in a little restaurant, where the victuals was served family style and the folks was more sociable.

Milt got to talking with a pretty girl, and come to find out she was raised on a farm down in Benton county, but now she lives in the hotel. She says it is kind of lonesome without no boy friend, but she likes a man that is growed up and sensible. Her and Milt got pretty friendly after that, and drunk a couple bottles beer together. Pretty soon she says, "Listen, Mister Wilson, my room is just down the hall from yours. Just leave your door unlocked, and after while I will slip down there, and them stuck-up hotel people don't need to know nothing about it."

The first thing Milt done was go in the barbershop and get a clean shave. He got his hair cut too, and told the barber to put some perfume on it. Then he bought a quart of good whiskey and took it up to his room. He put on his clean nightshirt, and went to bed just like the pretty girl said. He hid his wallet in one of his boots, so as not to take no chances. And then he just laid there and waited.

Pretty soon it was ten o'clock, but the pretty girl didn't show up yet. Milt took a couple drinks, and then he crawled back in bed and waited. After while he got up and drunk some more whiskey. It was right at eleven o'clock by this time, but people was still walking around in the hall, and Milt figured the pretty girl couldn't come till everything is quiet. So he just laid there and waited. And after while he went to sleep.

It was just getting light outdoors when Milt woke up. Soon as he found the wallet was empty he set up a terrible holler. The fellow at the desk says, "There ain't no pretty girls in the hotel, only two old ladies." He says, "A grown man ought to know enough to lock his door at night. And why didn't you give me your $600, so I could put it in the safe? It looks like you been drinking, and maybe you lost your money somewheres else, before you come to the hotel." Also he says, "Probably you didn't have no $600, anyhow. And if you don't shut up I will call the policeman, as we don't allow no hollering in here because the people is trying to sleep."

After while Milt went down to the restaurant and asked them about the pretty girl. But the restaurant man says he ain't seen a pretty girl for many years, and she was a cooch-dancer at the World's Fair in St. Louis, about 1904. Also he says if some apple-knockers has lost their pocketbook it ain't no skin off him, and he don't want to hear no more about it. Milt seen them people was all in cahoots, and there wasn't nothing he could do about it. So he just got on the train and come back home.

But ever since that time, Milt Wilson is always talking about how they got a very low moral tone in Joplin. He says Joplin is crowded with thieves and strumpets from all over the

35

country. God-fearing Christian folks had better keep away from a town like that, he says, and do their trading somewheres else.

WE CALL IT LAPLAND

ONE TIME there was several families come from back East somewheres, and homesteaded on the other side of Blytheville, Arkansas. It was pretty near fifty miles south of the Missouri line, but them peckerwoods thought they was living in Missouri. They went around saying, "You got to show me!" and bragging how Missouri is the garden spot of all creation. Most of them was poor ignorant people, not much better than Yankees if the truth was knowed.

After while the country got more settled up, and then a gang of government surveyors come out to put up stone markers. The homesteaders didn't pay no attention at first, but when they seen where the state line was marked they set up a terrible holler. The damn fools says they don't want to live in Arkansas, because the Arkansas climate ain't healthy, and the people in Arkansas can't read nor write. Also they says Arkansas is full of bears and panthers and copperhead snakes, so it ain't safe for civilized folks to stay there over night even. The surveyors tried to explain how the whole bunch had been a-living in Arkansas all this time, but it wasn't no use. Them people was so dumb they couldn't get it through their head.

Right in the middle of all this trouble, the head surveyor fell in love with a young widow-woman over on the St. Francis. The surveyors all boarded at her house, and she was the best cook in the whole country. The widow-woman says she was born and raised right here in Missouri, and it would break her heart to be surveyed out of her home. But nobody can make her live in Arkansas, no matter what happens. If the new line goes through she will sell out and move up North, even if she has to scrub floors for a living. And then she begun to cry. The head surveyor felt awful bad, and he didn't know what to do about it. Finally one of the other surveyors says, "Listen, chief, this is wild country, and Washington is a long way off. The land here ain't worth nothing, anyhow."

The head surveyor studied awhile, and finally he moved the state line markers fifty miles south, so as to make a big jog between the St. Francis River and the Mississippi. Then they run the line on out west somewhere, and pretty soon the head surveyor quit his job. He says to himself, "Well, twenty years from now some other surveyor will put the line back where it belongs. But me and the widow-woman will be dead by that time, so it won't make no difference."

Well sir, all that happened a long time ago, but the widow-woman's jog is still there. Her and the head surveyor got married all right, and raised a big family. Some of their great-grandchildren are living on the old farm, and the old farm is still in Missouri. Look at the map, and you'll see the southeast corner of Missouri sticking down like the heel of a boot, which is why some people call it the Boot Heel country. But us folks that live in Arkansas mostly call it Lapland, because it's the place where Missouri laps over into Arkansas.

There ain't no hard feelings about it nowadays. We don't begrudge them two counties to the Pukes, any more than we mind paying taxes for the lunatic asylum in Little Rock. Folks that don't want to live in Arkansas ain't quite right in their head, anyhow. It's better to keep people like that together in one place, rather than have 'em a-running around loose.

THE MAGIC WINDOW

ONE TIME there was an old farmer named Hobbes and he had a pretty daughter to keep house for him. The old man was in poor health. He was kind of silly, but he had sense enough to keep an eye on Julie, because she was crazy about the boys. When old man Hobbes got so feeble he couldn't do the chores, he hired a young fellow named Jake. But he got another man to cut a hole in the wall and put glass in it, like a little round window. It was fixed so anybody could set by the fire, and look out to the barn and the chicken-house and the woodpile. Whenever Julie went outdoors, the old man would watch through the glass, so he always knowed where she was at.

The first day the window was put in, Jake borrowed a goat from some folks down the creek, and turned it loose in the cow lot. Then he went in the house and looked out through the little window. "Paw Hobbes," says he, "I didn't know you had a goat." The old man says, "I ain't had a goat on the place for years." But when he looked out through his little window, there was a goat on the roof of the shed. That night Jake took the goat back where he got it.

Next day Jake took a straw hat and fastened it on a sow's head with baling wire. When old man Hobbes looked out through his little window, there was a hog walking around with a straw hat on. Julie was out there too, and when she come back in the house the old man says, "Did you see anything funny about that sow?" Julie says no, the old sow looked just the same as always. The old farmer didn't say nothing more, but he was considerable upset.

On the third day the old man looked out through his little window, and there was Jake walking down the lane without no pants on. You could see his long red drawers, and his shirttail a-flapping in the wind. But a minute later he run around the corner where the old man couldn't see him, put on his overalls, and come walking in with a armful of wood. "What do you mean, running around without no pants on?" says old man Hobbes. Jake just looked at him. "What are you talking about?" he says.

The old farmer thought about it awhile. "First goats, then hogs with hats on, and now men without no pants!" says he. "Jake, I believe that window is witched! Bust the glass out, and nail a board over the hole." Jake got the hammer and nailed up the window, so the old man couldn't see nothing out back of the house. After that him and Julie Hobbes went out to the barn whenever they felt like it, and done whatever they wanted to.

SHE'S GOT ONE SPOILED TIT

ONE TIME there was an old farmer that said he was a little hard of hearing. The truth is, he was so deaf he couldn't hear it thunder. His cow had strayed off somewheres, and the old man walked all around the country asking folks if they had seen her, but they all shook their heads. Finally he met up with a preacher, and he says to the preacher, "Will you tell all the church folks about my cow being lost?"

The preacher nodded his head to mean yes. So that night the old man went to church. He figured that when the people heard about the cow, he could maybe find out where she was saw last.

The sermon was pretty long, but the deef man set quiet till it was over. Then the preacher begun to tell the folks about a young couple that was going to get married. The fellow was a fine young man, he says. The girl was a teacher in the Sunday School, so the preacher laid it on pretty thick. He says this young lady is the cream of the crop and the flower of the flock and the pride of Durgenville, and then he says she is a fine sample of Christian womanhood and a inspiration to young people all over the country.

The old man couldn't hear a word, but he figured the preacher was telling the people about his cow. So pretty soon he got up and hollered, "Her rump's caved in, folks, and she's got one spoiled tit."

The preacher just stood there with his mouth open, as he had forgot all about the old cow. Some of the young folks pretty near died laughing. The girl begun to bawl, and the young fellow says he will kill that old bastard if it's the last thing he ever done. The meeting busted up in a terrible fight, and the sheriff grabbed the deef man and run for the jailhouse. The sheriff was in the church and heard the whole thing, so he figured the old man better be locked up for his own good.

It was away late in the night before things quietened down. Then the preacher and some other folks come to the jail and told the sheriff how it was. So they turned the old man loose, and a fellow that worked in the bank took him home in a buggy. Some folks say that the deef man never did get it through his head what all the trouble was about. The poor old fellow didn't come to town very often after that. He says everybody in the settlement is plumb crazy, and it ain't safe for a respectable citizen to go there nowadays.

THE YANK REUNION

ONE TIME the G.A.R. boys had a big reunion in our town, and there was old soldiers come from all over the country. Most of them was getting along in years, and there was lots of white whiskers a-blowing around. But every man had a little copper badge in his buttonhole, and lots of 'em wore blue coats with brass buttons. And every once in a while you would see a black hat with crossed sabers on the front, like they used to wear in the Yankee cavalry.

There was a few old soldiers had money to spend, but lots of them was busted. The folks that run the saloons and sporting houses would be glad to kick their ass right out in the street, but they was afraid to do it. Them old soldiers claimed if it wasn't for the Federal Army the whole country would have been ruined, so the people would be living in caves to this day, without nothing to eat only wild onions. It was as much as a man's life is worth to lay a finger on a veteran. He would just holler "Hog up! Hog up!" and more old soldiers would come a-running, to bust everything in the place. They wrecked the Red Onion Saloon, and smashed them big mirrors that cost seven hundred dollars. When some old fool lost his wallet at Blanche Tucker's whorehouse they swarmed in like hornets, and set the beds afire, and run the girls right out in their shirttail. They'd have burnt the house plumb down, if the firemen hadn't got there just in the nick of time.

Things looked so bad that lots of the businessmen just boarded up their store windows. The best people in town was mostly Southerners, and they just stayed in their houses. They locked the doors, and kept the children home from school. The only good thing about the reunion was that it only lasted three days. By that time the old soldiers was mostly sick and wore out, so pretty near all of 'em had went home.

On the fourth morning there was just one left, and he was a cripple. He'd got one leg shot off in the war, and his left arm was gone. His face was all scarred up, with a black patch over one eye. He set on the sidewalk in front of the First State Bank, and held out his big black hat with the crossed sabers on it. People was putting nickels and dimes in the hat, so the old soldier could get back to Iowa or wherever it was he come from.

Pretty soon old Colonel Fordyce walked out of the bank. He pulled out his wallet, and put a five-dollar bill in the hat. "Thank you, Comrade," says the old soldier. "Seems to me I seen you somewheres. Wasn't you a sergeant in the Ioway First?" Old Fordyce threw his shoulders back and turned red in the face. "No, sir!" says he. "I rode with Forrest's cavalry."

The crippled man looked at him kind of funny. "Mister," says he, "my own people give me nickels and dimes, or sometimes a quarter. But this is the first help I ever got from a Confederate. Would you mind telling me how-come you throwed in that five-dollar bill?" Colonel Fordyce grinned. "Not at all, sir. The sight of you does my old heart good.

You're the only Yank in this town that's trimmed up to suit me." And with that Colonel Fordyce walked down the street.

The old soldier just set there awhile, but he didn't say nothing. And pretty soon he got onto the northbound train, and that is the end of the story.

OLD MAN PRICE'S BOAR

ONE TIME there was a rich old man named Price, that owned the biggest farm on the creek. The Prices was a fine-haired family from Tennessee, and the old man didn't neighbor much with us common folks. The boys used to call him Biggoty Price, on account of holding his head so high, and thinking he was better than the common run. They was always telling jokes about him, down at the blacksmith shop.

Like when one of the Rickman boys come a-riding in, and everybody says what's the news? "There ain't nothing happened up our way," answered young Rickman, "only they had a hog-killin' over at the Price place." And then Bib Tarkey says somebody told him Biggoty Price has butchered a razorback boar that was seven year old. "Yes sir," puts in little Poody Henders, "the meat smelled so rank, all the folks down to Bosserman's Mill had to hold their nose!" The mill is pretty near two mile from Price's, and everybody knowed in reason that a hog couldn't stink that far. But all them fellows nodded their heads mighty sober, like it was true as God's own gospel.

"Yes sir," says Bib, "old man Price raised the biggest stink ever stirred up in these parts." All of them boys nodded their head again, solemn as a tree full of owls. "He sure did," says Bib, "and his two biggest gals got married that same week!"

Bib never cracked a smile when he said that, and neither did them fool boys he was a-talking to. But everybody else that heard it just laughed theirself sick. None of the folks ever did say just what was so funny about that story. It all happened a long time ago. But there's people in this town yet that will bust out a-laughing whenever something puts 'em in mind of the boar hog and them two big Price girls.

THE TWO WHITE SPRINGS

ONE TIME they caught a fellow red-handed in some great crime or other, and he was going to be hung sure. But everybody was crazy about riddles in them days, and the judge told the fellow if he made up a riddle that nobody in the court could answer, they would maybe turn him loose.

Well, there was a soldier's wife come to see this here criminal in jail, and says she will help him out. She took a wedding ring and put it on one of her tits, and the fellow sucked it and swallowed some milk. Then she put the ring on her other tit, and the fellow sucked milk out of that one, too. After while she told the fellow a riddle that nobody could answer:

> I got my dinner at two white springs,
> A-running through a yellow gold ring.

So when they brought him out in the trial room again, the fellow hollers to the judge, "I have thought up a riddle that nobody in the world can't answer." The judge didn't take no stock in it, because he knowed the champion riddlers of the country was in the crowd that day. But he says all right, just to give the man a chance to save his neck, and because all the big bugs wanted to hear the riddle. So the fellow says:

> I got my dinner at two white springs,
> A-running through a yellow gold ring.

All them heavyweight riddlers scratched their head and whispered to each other, but they couldn't make nothing out of it. After while some more folks come in, and the judge says, "Let's hear the riddle again." So the fellow sung out:

> I got my dinner at two white springs,
> A-running through a yellow gold ring.

The people thought and studied, but they couldn't see no sense in that riddle. After while the judge says, "Well, it looks like everybody has give up. If this man can tell the right answer, and show that it's a honest riddle, we'll have to let him go." So the fellow told the whole story. The judge made the soldier's wife stand up, to show how she put the ring on her tits. When the crowd seen it they just busted out laughing, and the judge turned the fellow loose.

The only one that didn't laugh was the soldier, because he was pretty mad to see his wife make a show of herself like that. The story don't say what him and her done from then on. But you can bet your life they didn't live happy ever after.

THEY ALL STARTED FROM SCRATCH

ONE TIME there was a horse trader married a Osage woman, and got rich when they struck oil in Oklahoma. He had five boys, and sent them all to college. But after they got through college he would not give them no more money. So the boys went to the city and made their own living. They was mostly salesmen or else worked in filling stations, and it was pretty hard sledding. They all married city girls that had went to college too, so naturally they didn't have no children.

The horse trader was getting pretty old, and the Osage woman was dead a long time ago. There was plenty of hired help to wait on him, but it was kind of lonesome in the big house. Also he got to worrying about something. He sent all the boys a ticket so they could bring their wife and come back home for Christmas. There was five nice bedrooms in the house, and the old man was fixing to throw a big old-fashioned Oklahoma party.

They had a fine time, and everybody ate turkey and drunk wine so they was feeling pretty good. After dinner the old man got them together in the big setting-room, with a log fire a-going. And then he says, "I am going to make a speech, and I want all of you to hear it." So everybody lit their cigarette and set down to listen. And then the old man says, "You are all healthy, and your wives is young. What I want to know is, how come I ain't got no grandchildren?"

Them five women looked at each other, and some of 'em giggled. The boys all looked straight at the old man, because they was Indians. After while the oldest one spoke up, and he says, "It takes money to raise families." The old man scowled. "Me and your maw didn't have a pot to cook in," he says. "We slept in a rawhide wigwam. We lived on wild onions and high wind. Sometimes the onions didn't hit, and the wind stopped a-blowing." The boys just set there poker faced, but the old man knowed what they was thinking about. "The first couple that shows me a live grandchild," says he, "I'll give 'em twenty-five thousand dollars cash. In small bills, and no tax to pay." With that he leaned back in the big leather chair, and shut his eyes.

Nobody said a word, but when the old man opened his eyes the boys and girls was gone. Pretty soon he pulled off his high-heeled boots, and walked down the hall in his sock feet. He listened a minute at every one of them bedroom doors, and then he grinned a little. "Them boys takes after their maw," says he. "Plenty of action, not much talk. I reckon they all started from scratch." And then he says something in the Osage language about rabbits. What it really means is, that there's always grass in the Territory, and water under the trees.

PINKLEY WAS A FOOL

ONE TIME there was a fellow named Pinkley Carr, that was always bragging about how much money he had. But the truth is Pinkley was just a crossroads gambler, poor as Job's turkey. Whenever he got hold of a few dollars he'd buy a new suit of clothes, or maybe a gold watch chain, or something like that. And then he would just kind of visit around, sponging off of his kinfolks that worked for their living.

The folks tried every way they knowed how to help Pinkley, but he wouldn't pay no attention. Finally it got so bad that even the peckerwood gals up on Salt Creek wouldn't go with him no more, because they seen he didn't have nothing but a loud voice and dry wind behind it. A fellow has got to be plumb ornery before them Salt Creek hussies will turn him down.

Pinkley got steamed up one Sunday, so he put on his best clothes. Then he borrowed a horse from his brother-in-law, and took off to the south end of the county, a-looking for women. Pretty soon a stranger was going the same way, so they rode along together. It wasn't no time at all till Pinkley begun to brag how much money he had. The stranger didn't say much, but Pinkley went on talking how he had just sold a big herd of cattle, and was carrying the gold in a belt round his middle. Pretty soon the stranger says, "Let's take this side road, because I know where a fellow has got some good whiskey hid." Pinkley says that suits him fine, so up the little road they went.

After while the road narrowed down to nothing, and they come to a lonesome place where there wasn't no house for miles around. The stranger drawed rein and dropped back a little. Then all of a sudden he pulled out his pistol and shot Pinkley Carr dead. Soon as he fell out of the saddle, the stranger got down and went through his clothes. But there wasn't no money-belt, and Pinkley didn't have only two silver dollars in his pocket. The stranger jerked out the fine gold watch chain, but there was just a little brass watch on the end of it.

That stranger had been a robber all his life, and he was pretty tough. Him and his pardners had killed many a man for their money, and never give it a second thought. But when he looked down at Pinkley he felt kind of sad, because if the damn fool hadn't lied about the money he'd be alive this minute. It didn't last long, though, and the robber was grinning as he got back on his horse. "If a growed-up man ain't got no better sense than that, he ought to be killed," says the robber. And with that he rode off, and left poor Pinkley a-laying there in the road.

The horse come home next day, but it was quite a while before they found the corpse. The folks wouldn't have knowed who he was, except for them fine clothes and the little brass watch. They buried him in the home graveyard, and the family felt pretty bad. The whole thing ought to be a lesson to the other goddam fools around here. It just goes to show that there ain't no use bragging how much money you've got. The facts of the matter is, it's just plumb silly.

WOMEN RUN WITH THE WOLVES

ONE TIME a bunch of old-timers got to talking about how panthers used to eat babies, even if they had to bust right into somebody's cabin or climb down the chimney to get it. Everybody knows that is the truth, but when a fellow says that wolves will eat babies too, the old hunters wasn't so sure. Panthers are mean like cats, but wolves belong to the dog family, and a good dog is pretty near human.

Another thing is that some of the old-time Indians claim they've got wolf blood in 'em. Not just by eating wolf-hearts neither, though that's mostly what they tell the white people. So then old Tandy Collins says, "Did you ever see a varmint that was half wolf and half man?" Everybody answers no, but several of us has seen Kiowas that look pretty wolfish, and some Comanches act worse than wolves. But they don't have no tails, and their hands and feet are just like anybody else. And when it comes to hair, they ain't as hairy as a white man.

Pretty soon a old hunter says that over in the Cherokee Nation if you find a bunch of wolf tracks, lots of times there will be human tracks along with 'em. Not made with moccasins on, but barefooted. And then he says if wolves find a baby boy they will eat him, but if it's a girl baby they carry her off alive, and maybe raise her with the wolf pups. There's men in the Territory that swear they seen naked women a-running with wolves on the range, and they didn't look like

50

Indians neither. And another fellow says he seen peckerwood gals running around naked as jaybirds right here in Missouri, but he don't think the wolves has got anything to do with it.

A man that used to drive the stage come along, and he says it ain't nothing uncommon to see one of them wild gals setting out in the brush, with wolf pups a-sucking her tits like a baby. And then they ask this fellow if he ever seen it with his own eyes. "No, I didn't," says he, "but my pappy told me *he* seen 'em." So then everybody wagged their head, because most of them had heard the Sooners telling big stories about such as that.

Finally old Tandy Collins says, "Well, even if we all seen gals with wolves a-sucking 'em, it don't prove that no human has got wolf blood in him. A baby will drink cow's milk, but that don't turn him into a dogie. And if a girl baby was raised up on wolf milk, that don't prove she's laying up with a he-wolf, does it? And even if she did, it don't mean she's going to have children by him."

Then another fellow begun to tell how some farm boys is always a-topping mares and heifers and nanny-goats. That kind of business is against the law nowadays, but everybody knows several boys has went to jail for it, right here in this county. "Well," says old Tandy, "did you ever hear of a mare foaling a colt that looked human?" The fellow says, "No, nor a heifer or a goat neither." The man that used to drive the stage says, "Them low-down boys don't bar nothing, and I wouldn't put a she-coyote past 'em, if they could catch her. And there's gals around here that is ornery enough to do anything. But I never knowed 'em to shell out no wolf pups," he says.

So then they got to talking about other things, like why a

squaw's dog has always got little scratches on its back, which is something for the doctors to figure out. Tandy Collins says the moon is at the bottom of them scratches, and that's the truth too, in a manner of speaking. It ain't got nothing to do with wolves, anyhow.

THE SILENT RIFLE

ONE TIME during the War Between the States all the young men in our town joined the army, and they had went off somewheres to fight the Yankees. There wasn't no men here at all only fellows that was too old, or else they was sick and crippled. But these old men got together and organized a militia company that they called the Home Guard. Old man Boaz was elected captain, because he had been in the Mexican War.

The Home Guards didn't have no uniforms, just their regular clothes. Captain Boaz wore his sword and his army pistol, but the rest of them carried shotguns and turkey rifles. They couldn't have no target practice because powder was scarce, but old Captain Boaz drilled 'em every day in front of the courthouse. He dug rifle pits, too, and had sentries a-marching up and down all night.

The first regular Confederate soldier to come back was young Tom Hopper, that got wounded at Oak Hill. Tom hobbled into town on crutches, and when he seen the Home Guards a-drilling he laughed till the tears run down his face. Nobody ever did find out what Tom Hopper was laughing about. They ask him for news of the war, and he told 'em the Yanks have invented a terrible new rifle that don't make no noise, but they could kill a man half-a-mile off. "I don't see how anybody can shoot without no noise," says old Captain Boaz. "It must work with a spring, like a crossbow," says Tom, "or else compressed air. That's what our officers think. I never seen a silent rifle close up, but I've heard the bullets whiz past my head more than once." Captain Boaz didn't say much, but you could see it give him something to think about.

About a week after that old man Ledbetter was standing in the courthouse yard, beside a big piece of sheet iron that the blacksmith set up for a sentry-box. All of a sudden come a loud "clang" when something hit the sheet iron. And there was a big old bullet a-laying on the ground. Old man Ledbetter took cover, and begun to holler "Yanks! Yanks!" Captain Boaz looked at that lead slug mighty close, and showed it to Tom Hopper. "It's a Yank bullet, all right," says Tom. "There's a sniper somewhere up on the mountain, with one of them silent rifles!"

Early next morning Captain Boaz stopped at the store, and just as he come out something whistled past his head and busted the window glass. Captain Boaz looked up at the mountain a minute, and then he ducked back into the store. There was a big bullet a-laying on the floor, just like the one that scared old man Ledbetter. When young Tom Hopper heard about it he says, "You better lay low, Captain. Them Yank sharpshooters always try to pick off whoever is in command. They can tell a officer by his walk, whether he's in uniform or not." Old Boaz looked kind of dubious, but he didn't return no answer.

Twice more that week Captain Boaz heard bullets mighty close, but he didn't hear no shot. The old man wasn't no coward, but this silent rifle business kind of got him down. The rest of them fellows was scared worse than Captain Boaz. Pretty soon they got to dodging whether they heard anything or not, and the whole company broke ranks when a humming-bird flew over their heads. They give up drilling altogether. Tom Hopper was so weak by this time that he couldn't hardly hobble down to the store, but he would laugh out loud to see the Home Guards a-skulking around behind buildings. The folks tried to keep Tom under cover, but he didn't scare worth a cent. Tom says he can't get well anyhow, and it ain't no use for a dying man to dodge bullets.

One day Tom Hopper fell right down in the street, and Captain Boaz seen that the boy was dying sure enough. "Where you hit, Tom?" says he. Tom just looked at him, and then he laughed right in the captain's face. It seemed like he tried to say something, but he couldn't quite make it, and pretty soon he was dead. There wasn't no fresh bullet hole in him, though. It was them old wounds he got at Oak Hill that killed Tom Hopper.

The folks give him a nice funeral, with the Stars and Bars on his coffin. The Home Guard didn't have no bugle, but they fired three volleys over the grave. Next day Captain Boaz went up to the shack where Tom had been sleeping, to see if he'd left anything that ought to be took care of. There was some old blankets, and two letters from a girl in Fayette-ville, and Tom's gray overcoat a-hanging on a peg. In one pocket of the coat the captain found a slingshot, like a kid's bean-flipper. And in the other pocket he found five big bullets, that Tom must have took off some dead Yankee.

Old Captain Boaz was pretty mad at first, but then he grinned a little. "Tom always liked a joke," he says to himself.

"An old soldier like me should have knowed better than to swallow that silent rifle story." Captain Boaz set on the porch awhile, and thought about the Home Guards a-hiding out from Yank riflemen. Then he throwed Tom Hopper's slingshot away back under the house, and never said nothing to the folks about it.

JACK AND THE GOWER

ONE TIME there was a settlement back in the hills, and the people had lots of cattle and hogs. They had fine orchards and garden patches with free range and the ground covered with acorns. Everybody built good houses, and there was a big spring right in the middle of town, and plenty of potatoes, and corn in the crib, and every smokehouse full of meat. Most everybody had a little silver hid somewhere, and even a few gold pieces. They had the world by the tail on a downhill pull, if it wasn't for the gower.

The gower was a monstrous big varmint that lived in a cave under the bluff. Kind of like a alligator, but forty foot long, and maybe ten foot high at the shoulder. They tried every way to get rid of it, but the critter's hide was awful tough. There wasn't no high powered rifles in them days, nothing but muzzle-loaders with plain lead bullets. If a gower was to show up now we could kill him easy with dynamite, but they didn't have no dynamite in that day and time.

Pretty near every day the gower would eat a whole hog. The folks was so well fixed they could spare him a hog every day in the year, and no hard feelings. But every once in a while the varmint would drag off a cow, and sometimes a horse that

55

was tied to the hitch rack. The folks tried leaving skinny old cows and wore-out horses right by the cave, but it wasn't no use. The gower would pass 'em up. He wouldn't touch nothing but the best. It got so that if a fellow had a fine cow he would hide it away out in the woods. The gower could trail good stock, just like a horse-jockey can smell out women.

The folks could maybe have stood losing hogs and cattle and even horses, but that wasn't the worst of it. Once every year, about the last of April, the gower would take a hankering for human meat. Then he come a-snuffing and a-blowing into town, looking for a pretty girl about sixteen years old. The girl's father and her brothers tried to fight him off with guns and axes. Then the gower would tear the house plumb down, and maybe kill the whole family. It always ended when the gower got the girl, and drug her off to his cave.

It is a bad thing for a family to lose their daughter that way, without even a corpse to bury. Lots of folks would put the kids in a covered wagon about the middle of March and go away off somewhere, until the gower had got somebody else's girl. Then it would be safe to come back and stay another year. Just like the people that live in the level lands down by some big river, and have to move out every year on account of the Spring floods.

There was a boy named Jack lived away up the mountain, and one day he found some people with a covered wagon a-camping beside the road. The oldest girl was the prettiest he ever seen all his life. So Jack would come down to the camp every day, and pretty soon he wanted to marry the girl, but her folks wouldn't hear of it because Jack didn't have no money. Finally they told him about the gower, but Jack says it is foolish for people to run away and leave their home on account of some fairy story like that. The man told him the gower is no fairy tale, and you can come to our settlement some time and see for yourself.

Jack says, "I have killed three bears and two panthers, and I ain't afraid of any varmint on earth. So I will come down there and kill this gower, soon as we get the corn laid by." The man just laughed kind of scornful. "Jack," says he, "if you kill the gower you can marry my daughter, and that ain't all. I'll give you a good farm with a new house on it. The folks will give you some hogs and cows and horses, too." And then the man laughed again, because he figured Jack couldn't kill the gower.

When Jack got home he told his folks about the gower, but they thought he must have got drunk, or else maybe he was losing his mind. So Jack went to see the blacksmith that lived up on Cooter Knob. He was a very wise old man, and he didn't laugh at Jack's story. Pretty soon the blacksmith reached under his bed and drug out the biggest shotgun you ever seen, with barrels four foot long. "Bullets ain't no good against gowers," says he. So then he took two white metal darts about a foot long, just big enough to fit the barrels. "They're made of silver, with a spell on it," he says. He went down to the shop and put steel points on them darts, and filed it down to a sharp point. "That steel," says he, "come out of a thunderbolt." The blacksmith cleaned the gun right good, and put ten drams of powder into each barrel, with a hornet-nest wad on top. Then in goes the silver darts, and a little more wadding so they won't fall out. "The way she's loaded, that gun will kill any varmint in the world," says the blacksmith.

When Jack got to the pretty girl's house she was glad to see him, and the old man looked considerable surprised. "There ain't nobody wants to get rid of the gower worse than me," he says, "but I am afraid you're a-riding to a fall. I advise you to go back home, and forget the whole thing." But Jack says no, he has done made up his mind to kill the gower, and that's all there is to it.

The first day the gower didn't show up, and the second day the varmint killed a cow at the other end of the settlement, but he was gone before Jack got there. On the third day the gower come a-walking right down the road, and Jack was ready for him. When the gower come a-lumbering past, Jack slid out from behind the house. *Ba*-LOOM! says the big shotgun. The gower was hurt bad, but the gun kicked Jack head over heels. He rolled backwards and got up, with the gower pretty near on top of him. The varmint had his mouth wide open, and teeth sticking out two foot long. *Ba*-LOOM! says the second barrel, right into the gower's mouth. The gun kicked Jack plumb senseless this time, but the gower had fell right down in the road. Every man in town was a-chopping on the varmint with axes by this time. But them silver darts is what killed the gower, and everybody knowed it.

Next day the citizens had a big meeting, and took up a collection to give Jack a lot of gold money. They give him a farm with a good house on it, and plenty of stock, too. Jack was a rich man now, so him and the pretty girl got married. Everything was all right from then on, and the whole bunch of 'em lived happy ever after.

HE WASN'T MY SON-IN-LAW

ONE TIME there was an old farmer come a-riding into town, and he acted kind of worried about something. He fooled around the wagon-yard awhile, and then

58

talked to the boys in the drugstore, but finally he went to the doctor's office. Him and Doc passed the time of day, and argued about crops and politics. Doc seen right away that the old man had something on his mind, but he never let on. So finally the old man got up to leave, and then he says, "Doc, I wish you'd come out to my place, soon as it's convenient."

The doctor picked up his little grip. "Sure, I'll go right now," says he. "Is Aunt Mary down with the rheumatism again?" The old man looked kind of funny. "No, Mary's doing fine," he says. "The truth is, I shot my son-in-law in the leg yesterday, and he ain't feeling very good."

Doc has got a name for minding his own business, but him and the old man was friends for forty years, so he spoke right up. "Ain't you kind of old for feuding, John? It don't look right, for a elderly gentleman like you to go around shooting his own kinfolks."

The old man knowed Doc didn't mean no harm, but he looked mighty uncomfortable just the same. "You don't understand, Doc," says he. "That boy warn't my son-in-law, when I shot him."

THE GHOST WAS STILL MAD

ONE TIME there was a fellow lived away down in Arkansas, and his name was Forrest. He was always bragging about how his family come of fighting stock. Maybe they did, at that. Him and his wife fit like cats and dogs. They would just cuss each other at first, but pretty soon they'd be throwing dishes, or else kick the glass out of the windows. And both of 'em kept a-hollering how they was going to kill

59

the other one. Them folks used to make such a racket that the neighbors couldn't get no sleep. The sheriff come down there two or three times, but soon as he was out of sight, Forrest and his woman would go to fighting again.

Things went on like that for several years, and then Forrest come to town all dressed up. He says his wife is dead, and he wants to buy the best goddam coffin they've got. Soon as the sheriff heard about it, he took Doc Holton out to examine the corpse. Everybody says Forrest must have killed her, but Doc couldn't find no mark on the body, nor no sign of poison. So he says she died of heart disease, and that's all there was to it.

After the funeral was over Forrest went away somewheres for about a week, and then he lived in the old house again. Everything was quiet till Sunday night, and then all hell broke loose just as the neighbors was coming home from church. You could hear hollering and cussing and dishes a-breaking and furniture being throwed around. "Well," says Aunt Sue Cartright, "Forrest sure didn't waste no time getting him another woman!" But just then somebody kicked the glass out of the window, and the folks could hear everything plain. You can believe it or not, but it was Forrest's wife that was making all that noise, and she was the loudest cusser in the whole country. The neighbors all knowed her voice, and they recognized them pet names she was a-hollering at Forrest. But everybody knowed that Forrest's wife was dead, and she had been laying in her grave for thirteen days.

The folks milled around out front for awhile, and then some of them busted right into the house to see what was going on. And what do you think? There was old Forrest setting in front of the fireplace, a-smoking his pipe. All that racket was out in the kitchen, and everybody could hear Forrest's wife a-cuss-

60

ing and hollering and throwing things around just like she always done. Forrest just set there in his rocking chair, and went right on a-smoking his pipe. "Don't get excited, folks," he says. "She ain't mad at nobody but me."

Forrest moved away soon after that, and the folks never did find out what become of him. Nobody ever heard any hell-raising there, after Forrest left. There was a lot of talk around town, though, and some people say the house is haunted to this day.

GOD DAMN THE WIND

ONE TIME there was a man in Oklahoma that wouldn't eat nothing only turtles. He tried to learn his dog to catch turtles, but the dog did not pay no attention. Then the man throwed his stick at the dog, and he says to the stick, "Beat the dog!" But the stick says, "I won't do it, only if you grease me with sidemeat."

The man went to a big old hog and he says, "Give me a piece of meat to grease my stick so it will beat the dog, because I am learning him to catch turtles." But the old hog says, "I won't do it, only if you feed me some acorns."

The man went to a big oak tree and he says, "Throw down some acorns to feed this hog, and then she will give me a piece of meat to grease my stick so it will beat the dog, because I am learning him to catch turtles." But the big oak tree says, "I won't do it, only if you make the sun shine warm on my back."

The man went to the sun and he says, "Shine warm on the tree's back so it will throw down some acorns to feed the hog, and then she will give me a piece of meat to grease my stick so it will beat the dog, because I am learning him to catch turtles." But the sun says, "I won't do it, only if you make the wind blow from the South."

The man went to the wind and he says, "Blow from the South and make the sun shine warm on the tree's back so it will throw down acorns to feed the hog, and then she will give me a piece of meat to grease my stick so it will beat the dog, because I am learning the son-of-a-bitch to catch turtles." But the wind says, "I won't do it." So then the man begun to cuss the wind, and he says, "God damn you and the sun both! Yes, and the oak tree too, also the hog and the stick and the dog and the turtles, and to hell with the whole business!" says he.

The man just stood there a-looking up, and he kept right on a-cussing the worst you ever heard. Pretty soon the wind begun to blow from the South, and the sun begun to shine warm on the oak tree's back. So then the oak throwed down some acorns to feed the hog, and the hog give the man a piece of meat to grease his stick. The stick begun to beat the dog, and the dog begun to hunt turtles. It wasn't no time at all till that dog got to be the best turtle catcher in the whole country. So then the man had all the turtles he could eat, and him and his family lived happy ever after.

THE LOOKING GLASS

ONE TIME there was a peckerwood named Zack that lived away out on the Carrencrow road, and he only come to town about twice a year. He always brung the old woman along, but she wouldn't never venture clear into town. If you asked Zack where was his wife, he'd say, "She only come as far as Straw Springs. Bess is kind of backward, and she don't like to mingle with city folks."

Bess was a terrible jealous woman, always afraid some town girl would get Zack away from her, though everybody

knowed there wasn't no danger. The boys used to tell how Zack got to drinking one day, and he paid ten cents for a little round looking glass, thinking it was a picture of his old daddy. On the way home he seen Bess was mad anyhow, and he was afraid she would give him hell for whooping off the ten cents. So he never showed her the looking glass, but hid it on a ledge in the shed room.

Every day Zack would look at that mirror awhile, and Bess knowed he was up to something, but she couldn't figure out what it was. She thought maybe he had a jug somewhere around the shed room. But finally she found the looking glass on a ledge, and seen her face in it. "So that's the hussy he goes to see in town!" says Bess. "My God, she's older than a tree, and ugly as a mud fence!" With that Bess begun to holler like a steam whistle. Zack tried to tell her it is just a picture of his pappy, but Bess says, "It's funny your pappy's got a sunbonnet on, and do you think I don't know a whore's picture when I see it?"

So then him and her got to fighting, and broke up pretty near everything in the shanty. Aunt Fanny Hall come over and tried to make peace, but when she found out that both of 'em thought the looking glass was a picture she busted out laughing. The boys say Aunt Fanny just kept on a-laughing till she couldn't stop, and had to be took home in the buggy.

It's just one of them funny stories, you understand. The chances are there ain't a word of truth in it. Fifty years ago there was plenty of folks around Carrencrow that didn't have nothing but feet on the ground, and maybe some of 'em never seen a looking glass in their life. But things is different nowadays, and there ain't a woman in this county but what has got one right in the house.

HARVEY AND MYRA

ONE TIME there was some people that didn't have but one boy in the family. Harvey was a good worker, and a big stout fellow besides. When he got to be seventeen years old it come in the boy's head to get married. His pappy was kind of worried, because Harvey done most of the farm work, but if he was to leave they'd have to pay a hired man. So pappy thought it would be better for Harvey to play around with some white trash gals up the creek, and not think about getting married for awhile yet.

But Harvey didn't take no interest in them peckerwood floozies, and he got to sparking a pretty girl named Myra that lived over in Lawrence county. Pretty soon it looked like him and Myra would get married sure, so the old man had to do something. "I hate to tell you this, son," says he. "Don't say nothing to your maw about it, but I was over in Lawrence county myself, fifteen years ago." What pappy meant was that he had knowed Myra's mother in them days. Harvey felt awful bad about this, but it won't do to marry your half-sister, so he quit going to see Myra.

It wasn't long till Harvey was going steady with another pretty girl that lived at Gum Springs, and her name was Virginia. But soon as the boy begun to talk about getting married, pappy says he had been over to Gum Springs fourteen years ago, so it won't do for Harvey to marry Virginia, neither. The boy done considerable grumbling this time, but he didn't want to hitch up with no half-sister, so him and Virginia quit going together.

One day the folks heard how Harvey is running after a girl named Kitty that was only thirteen years old, and she lives up near Neosho. And in about three weeks he begun to talk about getting married. So pappy dragged out the old story again, and says he was over there around Neosho thirteen years ago. "It would be sinful for a boy to lay up with his half-sister," pappy says, "and maybe against the law besides." Harvey didn't say much, but he done a lot of thinking.

Finally he went and asked his maw about it. "Marry whoever you want, son," she says. "Don't pay no attention to pappy. I don't believe he ever got all them women in trouble. But even if he did, it don't make no difference. The fact is, pappy ain't your father nohow." Harvey was kind of set back when he heard that. But pretty soon he seen the funny side of it, and him and maw both busted out laughing.

When the folks got up next morning Harvey was gone, and his saddle mare was gone too. They found out later that he had went back to Lawrence county, and fixed things up with Myra. So then him and her got married without no more foolishness, and they lived happy ever after.

FOUR ACES AIN'T GOOD

ONE TIME there was a fellow named McJimsey come to our town. He had plenty of money, because he owned a big newspaper somewhere. The boys got him into a poker game down at the fire station, but McJimsey played 'em so close to his belly that they couldn't do much with him.

Finally they got to playing draw, and old Doc Hemingway opened. Doc Hemingway wasn't no doctor, he was what they call a mechanic. McJimsey had three aces, so he raised Doc ten dollars. It was a pretty big raise, and everybody else took out. Doc held his hand kind of careless, and McJimsey leaned back in his chair, so he could see that Doc had three tens. McJimsey took one card, to look like he was maybe drawing to a straight, and he got the other ace.

McJimsey wasn't no fool, and he knowed them boys was crooked as a barrel of snakes. But he seen them three tens in Doc's hand, and he seen Doc draw two cards. He figured Doc couldn't possibly have nothing better than four tens. They didn't play no deuces wild in them days, and the joker wasn't no good only for aces, straights, and flushes. McJimsey studied them four aces, and he thought they was sure winners.

What McJimsey didn't know was that Doc throwed the ten of spades and the ten of hearts in the discard; he held the queen, jack, and ten of diamonds. And when Doc drawed, the dealer slipped him the king of diamonds and the joker. So Doc Hemingway had a straight flush, but McJimsey didn't have nothing but four aces and the king of spades. McJimsey hemmed and hawed awhile, and then he bet a hundred dollars.

Doc acted like he was terrible set back at first, but finally he fetched out his money. "Up five hundred," says he. Old man McJimsey studied a long time. Cold-deck or not, he knowed that Doc was holding three tens before the draw. He knowed Doc ditched two cards, and he'd been a-watching him mighty close. No matter if the deal was crooked, he figured there wasn't no way on earth the draw could have made Doc better than four tens.

The old man cussed and grumbled, but pretty soon he counted out five hundred smackers. "I call," says he. "Let's see you beat them four aces!" Doc Hemingway just grinned, and he says, "Four aces ain't good." So then Doc spread out his royal flush, and McJimsey was the sickest poker player you ever seen. He drawed a couple of deep breaths, and the sweat busted out on his forehead big as horse apples. It looked like the old man was going to have a stroke. "What went with them three tens?" says he. "I still got one of 'em," Doc says, and with that he raked in the pot.

Old McJimsey set there awhile, looking like he was made out of green soapstone. Them boys down at the fire station is mighty hard to beat. Pretty soon McJimsey walked out, and he ain't never been back since.

TOBEY THE KINGSNAKE

ONE TIME there was a fellow named J. Frank Tooler, and he heard folks talking how a kingsnake can kill a rattlesnake easy. The old-timers say that kingsnakes put in most of their time a-hunting rattlers and killing 'em just for the hell of it. The story don't sound reasonable, because a kingsnake ain't got no poison, so it looks like the rattler would just bite the kingsnake once and that would be the end of it. J. Frank didn't go so far as to call anybody a liar, but he says he is going to try a experiment and settle the question once and for all.

The first thing he done was to catch a kingsnake and put it in a wire cage. He named it Tobey after our sheriff, which was a kind of a joke because the sheriff was scared to death of snakes. The whole Tooler family had to catch mice for the critter to eat, and it was considerable of a chore. J. Frank told the boys next time you find a rattler don't kill him, but just holler for me.

Things run along for quite awhile, and then one of the hands run onto a big yellow rattlesnake in the pasture. Soon as he heard the hollering, J. Frank grabbed the cage and run down there. When they turned Tobey loose he didn't pay no mind to the rattler at first. No sir, that kingsnake just went a-slithering around, sticking out his tongue and looking at the bushes. All of a sudden Tobey stopped in front of a little bunch of snakeweed, and wiggled as if to say, "That's what I been a-looking for!" And then he give a big jump and grabbed the rattlesnake.

There was brush tore up and bushes bit for a couple of minutes, and then the old rattler socked his fangs into Tobey. But Tobey just run back and bit off a chunk of snakeweed. Soon as he swallowed a leaf or two, the kingsnake was just as good as ever, and he tackled the old rattler again. And that's the way things went from then on. The rattler bit him four times, but a swallow of that weed was all it took to cure the poison. And finally Tobey killed the old rattler plumb dead, and then crawled back into his cage to rest up.

Well sir, J. Frank took the kingsnake all round the neighborhood after that, showing off how it could kill rattlesnakes. Tobey never would tackle a rattler till he seen a bunch of snakeweed a-growing right handy. Folks come for miles around to see them fights, and sometimes they would bet on the rattler. But Tobey always killed 'em, even if it took six or seven swallows of snakeweed to do the job.

Finally a fool boy from Burdock township pulled up the weed and moved it about thirty feet, just to see what would happen. Nobody paid no attention, because they was all watching the fight. But just then Tobey got bit, so he come a-slithering back to get a dose of snakeweed. And when he seen the weed was gone, Tobey just give up. J. Frank run to fetch the weed back, but it was too late. Poor Tobey took a spasm, and pretty soon he was dead as a doornail.

Some fellows up the creek got to catching kingsnakes and matching 'em to fight rattlers, but J. Frank never took no more interest in it after Tobey died. J. Frank says the experiment worked out just like he figured. There ain't no doubt that a kingsnake can kill a rattler all right, if he's got plenty of snake-weed handy to cure the poison.

HELL AMONG THE CHICKENS

ONE TIME there was a farmer that was just going to bed, when he heard something out by the chicken house. They'd been losing poultry right along, and the farmer didn't stop for no clothes. He just grabbed the shotgun and run out there, without nothing on only his long wool underwear. He seen the chicken house door was wide open, so he cocked both hammers. Everything was quiet now, so the farmer just squatted down and waited, with the gun pointed right at the chicken house.

You know how old-fashioned underwear is made, so that when a fellow hunkers down the drawers kind of open up in the back? Well, the farmer was a-watching for some varmint in the henhouse, and he didn't pay no mind what was going on behind him. Just about that time the old hound dog come around the corner, and stuck his snoot right in the place where them drawers gapped open. When the farmer felt that cold nose he let out a yell and jumped six foot high. Naturally, both barrels of the gun went off.

The farmer's wife come a-running out with a big lantern and there was her man down on his hands and knees. It looked like he had throwed the gun ten foot ahead of him, and the

old hound dog was capering round regardless. Soon as she seen the farmer wasn't hurt, the old woman run over to the chicken house. There was dead chickens all over the place, and the walls plumb riddled with turkey-shot, so naturally she raised hell. And then the farmer begun to holler how somebody has goosed him from behind, and the gun went off accidental.

The woman talked mighty nasty, and she says, "You must have dreamed the whole thing, because there ain't nobody around here but me. And now you've killed my laying hens, with eggs forty cents a dozen, and pretty near ruined the chicken house besides." The farmer had figured out what happened by this time, but he never let on to the old woman. Him and her stayed up pretty near all night, a-picking and cleaning chickens. She kept right on talking about what a fool anybody is to do a trick like that, and it sure did get tiresome.

Them people had chicken stewed, roasted, fried and boiled for quite awhile, but it was mighty dry meat, as the old saying goes. And even to this day, the farmer feels kind of foolish every time he sees all them bullet holes in the chicken house.

GABE SAYS IT AIN'T SO BAD

ONE TIME a fellow named Wes Adams met up with old Gabe Ledbetter in the road, and they hadn't saw each other for a long time. So they shook hands, and Wes says, "How are you making out these days?" Gabe looked mighty solemn. "I'm a-living on Hockey Mountain," says he, "and pretty far up, at that. I got married a couple of years back."

Wes Adams thought any woman must be out of their head to marry old Gabe Ledbetter, but the idea tickled him anyhow, so he says, "That's good."

"It ain't so good as you might think," Gabe says. "My wife come of a no-account family, and she brought me a lot of grief."

"Well, that's bad," says Wes Adams.

"It ain't so bad as you might think," Gabe says, "because she was pretty well fixed. I made her give me seven hundred dollars before we got married."

"Well, that's good," says Wes.

"It ain't so good as you might think," Gabe says, "because I put the money in sheep, and the goddam wolves eat 'em up."

"Well, that's bad," says Wes Adams.

"It ain't so bad as you might think," Gabe says, "because I killed forty-three of them wolves, and there's a thirty-dollar bounty on wolf scalps now."

"Well, that's good," says Wes Adams.

"It ain't so good as you might think," Gabe says, "because the house caught fire while I was in town to get the bounty, and burnt plumb to the ground."

"Well, that's bad," says Wes.

"It ain't so bad as you might think," Gabe says, "because my wife was in the house, and there ain't nothing left of her but a tubful of ashes and a few black bones."

Wes Adams started to say "Well, that's good," but he stopped himself. It didn't seem hardly decent, when a man's wife has been burnt to death, so he just stood there with his mouth open.

"She had some life insurance, too," says Gabe, "and the house wasn't worth much, anyhow. It ain't so bad as you might think," he says. So then Gabe Ledbetter just waved his hand, and walked on down the road.

The way Wes tells it, his head was spinning round like a top by that time, and he couldn't think of nothing more to say.

Gabe Ledbetter always looked solemn as a judge, but he couldn't help cracking jokes like that. The facts of the matter is, Gabe hadn't never been married at all. He never kept no sheep, and if he ever killed a wolf the neighbors never heard tell of it. And his house didn't burn down, neither. The truth is, he never did have no house.

THE BOOGER DOG

ONE TIME there was a fellow that believed in all kinds of signs and omens, so he couldn't get no rest at all. Whenever he seen something out of the ordinary, he figured the Devil must be at the bottom of it, or maybe witches. You take a fellow that believes them things, and he is always worried about something or other. He spends half his time cooking up charms, and quoting verses out of the Bible, and burying stuff at the crossroads, and making marks on the front door, and all such as that.

Well, this fellow got to worrying about a big black dog that come around the house every day. Nobody in the neighborhood had a dog like that, and he thought there was something spooky about it. Finally he fixed up a big dose of strychnine, and put it in a piece of meat. The black dog gobbled up the bait, and then it had fits. When he seen the black dog laying there the fellow was sorry he done it, because maybe it was just a natural dog after all. But when he went out to milk next morning, there was the big black dog a-frisking round just as lively as ever.

What really happened was that he put too much strychnine in the meat. Everybody knows that if you feed a wolf too much poison it makes him sick right away, so he will throw it up and get well. The neighbors tried to tell the fellow about this, but he didn't take no stock in it. From that time on he figured the varmint was a booger dog, that couldn't be killed with poison nohow.

74

Next time the black dog come up close to the house, the fellow give it both barrels of his shotgun. And while the dog laid there a-kicking, he run out with the chopping-axe and cut its head right off. "Maybe that will settle your hash," says he. And then the fellow went to bed, with the door barred and the latchstring pulled in. But away along in the night he heard something outside. The moon was shining bright, and there was the booger dog a-running around lively as ever, carrying its head in its mouth! When the neighbors heard that one they all just laughed like fools, and the fellow got so mad he wouldn't talk about it no more.

That same week he seen the booger dog with its head back on the same as ever, so the fellow got him a silver spoon and hammered out a big slug. He loaded up his gun, with the silver bullet instead of shot. When he pulled the trigger this time, the black dog fell over just like it done before. Then the fellow carried brush and poles, and built a great big fire out by the gate. When the fire got to going good he drug the dead dog out there, and throwed it in the fire. He just kept a-piling on wood till the carcass was burnt plumb to ashes. Then he went to bed, so scared he couldn't get much sleep. But after two days went past without no sign of the booger dog, the fellow got to feeling pretty good again.

About a week later some of the neighbor boys come over, and they wanted to know how he is getting along with the booger dog. The fellow told 'em what happened, and they went and stirred around in the ashes a long time. When you burn up a common carcass there's always a few black bones left, and some teeth. So when the boys couldn't find nothing only wood ashes, they began to feel kind of spooky. They all knowed in reason that a natural dog couldn't carry it's head in its mouth, like the fellow said. But if the varmint was a genuine booger dog, it is something else again.

There is lots going on in this world that people don't know about, like them miracles in the Bible, so the boys figured the booger dog story might be true, after all. It ain't no use to argue about things like that, anyhow.

AN INNOCENT MAN

ONE TIME there was an old man and his wife died, so pretty soon he took up with a girl that was only thirteen years old. The kinfolks didn't like it, because they says a man seventy years old won't do no good with a woman that is only thirteen years old. And they says she is not big enough to be married yet, also you are too old to raise a family. And if she was to have a baby, when the baby is ten years old you will be eighty. And if a man is eighty years old, how is he going to make a living for a young wife and a ten-year-old boy?

The old man says you folks don't need to worry, because Rosie and me ain't going to have no children. And the folks says how do you know there won't be no children? The old man says them is family matters, and I do not choose to talk about things like that, whether they are kinfolks or not. And he says you just go home and tend to your own business, and leave me and Rosie alone.

Things went along all right for awhile, and him and Rosie was doing fine. And then one day Rosie says she is going to have a baby. The old man just laughed, and he says, "It ain't no such a thing." But after while it looked like Rosie is going to have a baby sure enough, and the old man got mighty low in his mind, because he knowed he'd done wrong, and here was Rosie knocked up. The more he worried the worse he felt. The old man thought about it a long time, and finally he made up his mind what to do. So then he says, "Rosie, I am going to town, and I won't be home till dark." And Rosie she says all right.

The old man walked off down the road, but he didn't go to town. He sneaked around through the woods and come into the barn by the back way. Pretty soon he looked through a crack, and seen Rosie come out and throw a clean quilt on the fence. The old man set down awhile, then he climbed up and fastened the rope to a rafter. He tied a slipknot in the rope, and climbed part way up the ladder. Then he put the noose round his neck, and he says, "Well, here goes nothing. May the Lord have mercy on my soul!" But just as he started to jump off the ladder, the old man heard Rosie a-squealing up at the house. So he took the rope off his neck and went to see what was the matter.

Well sir, when he come around the corner of the house there was Rosie and one of the neighbor boys, laying on a quilt right out in the yard. They was carrying on something scandalous. And every little bit Rosie would squeal like a young pig. When she seen the old man a-standing there she hollered louder than ever. And then Rosie jumped up and run into the house.

The old fellow just stood there, a-scowling at the neighbor boy. "Young man," says he, "I believe you look better with pants on." And so the neighbor boy got up and put on his overalls. And then the boy says, "It ain't my fault, Mister. I don't never come over here only when Rosie hangs a quilt on the fence. She told me you had went to town." Just then Rosie come out of the house a-crying how she's got to have a divorce, and the neighbor boy says, "Me and Rosie wants to get married." The old man says, "Well, there ain't nobody stopping you. And you don't need no divorce, because them papers behind the clock ain't nothing but tax receipts, but Rosie can't read and so she thinks they are wedding papers." Rosie began to holler again when she heard that, but pretty soon the neighbor boy got her quietened down. And then him and her went to town and got married.

When the old man's kinfolks come over that evening, he was still a-setting on the steps. "You better let us put you to bed, pappy," says the womenfolks, "because it's been kind of a hard day." The old man just looked at them. "You ain't got no idea," says he, "how close I come to hanging a innocent man." The folks all shook their head, because they thought the old fellow was a-wandering in his mind. So he just looked at 'em again, and never said no more about it.

GOOD COUNTRY
BUTTERMILK

ONE TIME there was a man named Colonel Ficke come out from St. Louis, and he was a government gauger. His job was to ride around the country looking at still houses, and test the whiskey they was making. The law was different in those days, so that farmers had a right to make liquor and sell it. A man could run a still just the same as a gristmill or a cotton gin, if he paid his taxes and the whiskey was good enough to suit the gauger.

This man Ficke was riding along with the Superintendent of Schools, and his name was Colonel Prather. It seems like pretty near every man that amounted to anything was a colonel in the early days. Both of the colonels was hungry, and they come to a little log cabin. There was a woman and a lot of children, and the woman was a-churning. She didn't seem to have any victuals handy, and wasn't very clean anyhow, but she brought out two tin cups so they could drink some buttermilk. Colonel Ficke says it is the finest he ever tasted, lots better than what they have got in St. Louis. He says that's the way he likes buttermilk, fresh from the churn with good big chunks of butter in it.

Just then a little boy run out of the house a-yelling, "Maw, that man's got my cup!" and he pointed at Colonel Ficke. The woman says, "Never mind, son, he'll give it back pretty soon." But the little boy kept a-hollering. "It's my special cup, Maw! The one I was keeping the dog-ticks in!" Colonel Ficke just stood still a minute, and he turned kind of green around the gills. Then he staggered out to the gate, and puked up the buttermilk. By the time Colonel Prather got there, Colonel Ficke was on his horse a-galloping back towards the settlement.

When Colonel Prather got home he told the family about what happened, and he laughed loud enough to knock shingles off the roof. But the folks couldn't see anything funny about a man drinking buttermilk with dog-ticks in it. Colonel Prather's wife says, "Stories like that are disgusting, enough to make a body sick to their stomach. People that laugh at such things have got mighty strange ideas about what's a joke," she says. But Colonel Prather just laughed louder than ever when he heard that. All the rest of his life Colonel

Prather told it for a fine comical tale, and he didn't care if anybody else laughed or not.

WHAT THEY TOLD
ON JASPER

ONE TIME there was a boy named Jasper that lived up on Crane Creek, and he used to act kind of silly sometimes. So whenever anybody wanted to tell a chuckle-head story, they would generally lay it on Jasper. The boys didn't mean no harm by it. Everybody knowed that Jasper never really done all them things, but they never let on. Tales like that was considered a great joke, in the early days.

Jasper's own uncle used to tell about the time they was going to have a birthday party in town. Some hightoned people was coming from Springfield, so the old woman told Jasper he better pour a gourdful of water over his feet, because he'd been plowing all day. "Shucks," says Jasper, "if I got to dude myself all up, I'd just as lief not go to their damned old party!"

There was a big ironwood tree down by the road, and the tourists was always a-gawking at it. A ironwood don't look like no common tree, because the trunk ain't round. One time a fellow from St. Louis got out of the hack, and he examined the big ironwood mighty careful. Jasper was a-standing there, and the man asked him what kind of a tree it was. "Well, sir," says Jasper, "there ain't no name for that there tree. There's plenty of 'em a-growing hereabouts, but the folks ain't got around to naming 'em yet."

Another time Jasper took a notion to go fishing, and used

minnows for bait, but he didn't catch nothing. "No, I didn't get ary bite," says Jasper, "but the day wasn't plumb wasted." Pretty soon somebody asked how he figured it wasn't wasted. "Well," says Jasper, "I fetched my minners home and fed 'em to the chickens."

Jasper felt as bad as anybody when his Uncle John got killed, but that didn't stop him from making a funny joke about it. When they was dividing up the old man's property, a big solemn lawyer says, "How long has your uncle been dead?" Jasper scratched his head and counted on his fingers. "Well," he says kind of doubtful, "if Uncle John had lived till Tuesday, he'd be dead three weeks." The big lawyer just looked flabbergasted for a minute, and then he grinned. "If I'd asked a few more questions," he told the boys later, "Jasper would have had me counting on my fingers, too!"

When the new schoolmarm come to Crane Creek they had considerable trouble with Jasper. She always asked him the easiest questions to save argument, also wear and tear on religion. But when it come to spelling, her and Jasper never did get along. Jasper told her right off that he wouldn't spell 'taters with a *p*, no matter what's in the book. He says if she ain't got no more sense than that, she better stay home and make soap. Also Jasper says it stands to reason that women don't know enough to teach a school, anyhow.

One time Jasper was fixing to marry a girl that wasn't very well thought of, and his paw was trying to talk him out of it. "Listen, Jasper," says the old man, "don't you know that gal has laid up with every man in town?" Jasper thought awhile, and then he says, "Well, it ain't a very big town." The girl's folks went right ahead with their plans, and they got the preacher there all right, but Jasper never showed up. The kinfolks waited awhile, and then a couple of boys rode over to see what was wrong. There was Jasper, a-setting on the porch. The boys begun to raise hell, but Jasper just says, "Well, it was a-raining so hard, I just figured they'd put the wedding off." So then the girl's pappy says he don't want no half-wit for a son-in-law, and Jasper was well rid of the whole business.

When the railroad come through in 1904 there was a bunch of foreigners moved in, and they had a big green parrot. It was the first parrot ever come to this county. When Jasper happened to walk by the foreigners' house, there was the parrot a-setting on the gate. Jasper just gawked at it for a minute, and then he edged up close like he was going to grab the critter. The parrot opened its mouth and says, "Come in, brother." Jasper jumped back like somebody had shot at him. "My God," says he, "I thought you was a bird!"

Jasper had got an old brass-mounted pistol somewhere, and he claimed it belonged to his great-grandpappy that was at King's Mountain when they licked the British. Jasper says it is a valuable relic in the family, and he's going to give it to his oldest son. So then somebody says, "Why, Jasper, you ain't got no son. You ain't even married yet." Jasper says he will get married someday, and have a son. "But what if you don't never have any children?" says old man Hawley. "It ain't by no means likely," says Jasper. "But if I don't have no children, I'll just leave that gun to my *grand*children."

Judging by the tales they used to tell on Jasper, you'd think he would come to a mighty sorry finish. But the fact is, Jasper heired a good farm, and married one of the Pinkley girls, and raised a fine big family. Which is a lot more than you can say for some of the boys that told them fool stories about him.

82

PAW WON'T LIKE THIS

ONE TIME there was a farm boy coming to town with a big load of hay. Just after they crossed the Cow Creek bridge the horses got to acting up, and pretty soon they upset the whole business in the road just below the Applegate place. When old man Applegate come out there was the wagon laying on one side, and a pile of hay big as a mountain. The farm boy was running around wild-eyed, and looked like he was going to bust out crying. "Paw won't like this," says he. "Paw won't like this at all!"

As soon as he seen the horses wasn't hurt, old man Applegate done his best to get the boy calmed down. "Don't you worry, son," says he. "It ain't your fault. Things like that might happen to anybody." So then he says, "You just fetch the team up to my barn, and come and eat dinner with us. After dinner me and the hired man will help you pitch that hay back onto the rack." The boy says he'd like to have dinner, but his paw wouldn't want him to leave the wagon. "Don't you worry about that," says old man Applegate, "I've knowed your paw longer than you have, and I'll tell him all about it." So the boy took his team up to the barn, and fed them. And then he went over to the house and eat a big dinner with the family.

After dinner they all set out on the porch awhile, a-belching and picking their teeth. Everybody tried their best to cheer the boy up, but he acted terrible uneasy. "Paw won't like this," says he, "I better go back to the wagon." The folks just laughed, and says for him not worry. "The first time I see your paw, I'll tell him you ain't to blame," says old man Applegate. "Maybe I'll tend to it this evening. Is your paw in town today?"

The boy looked at old man Applegate kind of bewildered. "Why no," he says, "paw's under that there hay."

THE LAZY FARMER

ONE TIME there was a fellow named Isham Byrd, and everybody says he is the laziest man in the whole country. Whenever the folks come along the road you could see Ish laying out on the porch with his mouth open, or else he was hollering for the old woman to shoo the flies off him. The boys used to tell how the doctor thought maybe Ish don't get enough sleep, so that's why he is always so tired. "Well, I sleep fine at night," says Ish, "and I sleep pretty good of a morning, too. But between high noon and sundown, it seems like I can't get no rest at all. Just roll and tumble and have bad dreams."

Ish wouldn't do no work at all mostly, because he argued that there is a time for everything under the sun, and unto each a season thereof, which is in the Bible. "Work is a good thing in its place," says he, "but this here toiling between meals ain't healthy."

His own brother used to tell about the time Ish happened to set down in a bunch of prickly pear cactus. Most fellows would have jumped up mighty quick, but not Ish. No sir, he just set on them stickers and hollered bloody murder. Ish Byrd was a man that would rather holler than get up. That's what his brother Jeff says, anyhow.

A fellow come along one day and he was giving away tin pans to the people if they would buy ten pounds of flour. "I got a fine present for you, brother," says the peddler, "free gratis for nothing, and it won't cost you a cent!" Ish Byrd never moved, except to open one eye. "Just leave it on the table," says he. The peddler started to talk about the flour, but Ish just shut his eye and went back to sleep. Pretty soon he began to snore, so the fellow just give up and went on to the next house.

The story goes that the time Hoover was President, the neighbors was going to bury Ish, just to keep him from starv-

ing to death. They put him in a coffin and started for the graveyard. A stranger come along and seen what they was doing. "Good Lord, gentlemen," he says, "you can't bury this man when he ain't dead!" The boys all looked solemn. "There ain't nothing else to do," they told the stranger, "because he won't work, and there ain't a grain of corn on his place." The stranger thought they was in dead earnest. "Before I'll see a man buried alive, I will give him a whole wagon load of corn," says he. Ish raised his head up out of the coffin. "Stranger," he says, "is that corn shucked?"

Some of them loafers down at the store could talk all day about how lazy Ish Byrd was, and never repeat theirself once. Most of the stories was just made-up tales, of course. But it's a fact that Ish wasn't no ball of fire, when there was any hard work to be done.

A PRIVATE ROOM

ONE TIME there was a man from Kansas City come down here, and built him a big hotel right beside our new highway. It was kind of a novelty in this part of the country. Every little town around here had two or three houses where they rented rooms and took in boarders, but the folks didn't know much about regular hotels. The Kansas City man done pretty good with the tourists in the summer time, and there was a few drummers come every week. But mighty few of the home folks ever set foot in the big hotel.

Sometimes a fresh married couple would go there, if the boy had money and wanted to show off. They used to tell about a young fellow that lived up on Greasy Creek, and he married one of the McCanse girls. Soon as the knot was tied they walked out of the courthouse and went to the big hotel. When they got up to the desk the boy says: "Mister, have you got any private rooms here?" The hotel man told him yes, sir. "Well," says the young fellow, "we want the best room you've got. I don't care what it costs, so long as it's private." The hotel man called the bellboy, but they wouldn't ride in the elevator, and the girl wouldn't let go of her satchel. The bellhop walked them upstairs, turned on the lights, and brought a picher of ice water.

Pretty soon the boy from Greasy Creek come back downstairs, and he was pretty mad. "Look here," he says, "didn't I tell you we wanted a private room?" The hotel man just gawked at him. "That's what I gave you, and it's the best room in the house," says he. "Hell's fire, it ain't private!" the boy hollered. "Why, there's a toilet up there! Folks will be running in and out all night!"

The hotel man was about to bust out laughing, but it's lucky he never done it. That Greasy Creek boy thought he was being took advantage of, and he wasn't in no mood for jokes. If anybody had laughed right then, there might have been bad trouble. So the hotel man went upstairs himself, and showed the boy how things was. "The whole thing is private, bathroom and all," says he. And then he showed the young folks how to lock the outside door, so nobody could get in. Everything was all right after that, and no more complaints from the honeymooners.

The bellhop told a couple of drummers, and the story got around. Most people thought it was just a made-up tale, like the one about the traveling salesman and the farmer's daughter. But that was because they hadn't never been up on Greasy Creek. The home folks didn't see nothing unreasonable about it.

87

BRAINS FOR A TANNER

ONE TIME there was an old fellow named Johnny Hutchinson walking home with a little sack of meal, when here come seven Yankees a-riding South. They took the old man's meal, and then they searched him, but he didn't have no money. Old man Hutchinson was a terrible stupid fellow, but kind of loud-mouthed because he used to be a schoolteacher. Probably he cussed 'em out, or something. Anyhow, them Yankees killed him. Next morning the women-folks found him laying there in the road, with three bullets in his chest.

One of them Yankees was shot down in Arkansas about a week after that, and young Jim Hutchinson went down there to see him. The fellow knowed he was a-dying, and he told Jim the names of the other Yanks that was there the day Johnny Hutchinson got killed. Jim checked up on them six names, and he found out that the fellow had told the truth, because every one of 'em was seen in the neighborhood the same day. They was wearing Federal boots and britches, but not one of 'em was regular enlisted in the Yank army. They was just a bunch of bushwhackers, a-roaming around to steal whatever they could find.

Jim didn't do much talking, but it wasn't long till one of them fellows was found dead, laying in the road just about where old Johnny Hutchinson was killed. There wasn't no blood on the ground, so it looked like he'd been shot some-wheres else, and the corpse hauled down there in a wagon. A few weeks later another dead Yank showed up in the same place, with his throat cut from ear to ear. "Two down and four to go," says young Jim Hutchinson.

Them four fellows laid low for awhile, but then one of 'em got to fighting with some Cherokee people over at Southwest City, and a woman smashed in his head with one of these iron bootjacks they was using for a doorstop. The three that was left stuck mighty close together after that, because they knowed young Jim Hutchinson was on their trail. One day they was standing in the street when Jim come a-riding into town. They killed his horse at the first fire, but Jim was a-shooting before he hit the ground. The crowd scattered like leaves in a wind, but two of them Yanks laid there dead, and the other one was a-dying. Jim was hit twice, but they was both flesh wounds. A deputy marshal got shot in the foot, and several citizens was scared out of a year's growth, but otherwise there wasn't no harm done.

A fool woman run out in the street, and she says, "My goodness, why did you shoot all those men?" She was from up North somewheres, and didn't know any better than to ask questions like that. Jim seen she didn't mean no harm. "I'm tanning a groundhog hide, ma'am," says he, "and it takes three or four Yankees to furnish the material." The woman just stood there with her mouth open, because she couldn't make out what he was talking about. She told the doctor that poor Mister Hutchinson must be hurt pretty bad, because he acted kind of delirious.

The home folks understood what Jim meant, and they was laughing about it all over town. We all tanned our leather Choctaw style, in them days. You just scrape the fat off, and rub a spoonful of fresh brains into the flesh side of the skin.

89

THEY MOVED THE
GRAVEYARD

ONE TIME the government was building a big dam on the river, and all the people that lived in our town had to move out, because pretty soon the whole place would be under water. The old folks done a lot of grumbling, but the government paid everybody a fair price for their property, so they didn't have no real kick a-coming.

Some folks put their houses on rollers and moved them up to a new town on the hill, but most of 'em just tore the buildings down and saved the best lumber to build a new house. Lots of people hauled stone from the old foundations, and bricks out of the chimneys, and sheet-iron roofs, and all kinds of stuff. They moved pretty near everything they had, except deep wells and cyclone cellars.

The old-timers set up a terrible squawk about the graveyard. The government laid out a big cemetery in the new town, with a nice lot for each family. Then a gang of foreigners come to dig new graves and move the corpses. They moved every gravestone too, and fixed everything up in good shape. But the old settlers didn't like to have their folks dug up and hauled around that way, and they was afraid them foreigners might get the corpses mixed up.

There was one old woman that her husband had been dead twenty-five years, and she aimed to be buried right beside him. She kept thinking how awful it would be if the foreigners put the wrong corpse under his tombstone, and there she'd be a-laying up with somebody she didn't even know who it was.

And what if they was to bury one of them no-account Tollivers in her man's place, when everybody knowed she hated a Tolliver worse than rattlesnakes! Nothing would do but her brother-in-law must be there when they dug up the corpse. And she told him to look careful and make sure it was the right man. And then he was to ride along with the corpse, and not come home till he seen them bury pappy in the new grave, with the old headstone on top. The brother-in-law grumbled a good deal, but finally he says he will do it.

The brother-in-law was gone till away in the night, but when he got home the whole family was setting up a-waiting for him. He looked pretty glum, and the first thing he done was to take a big drink of whiskey. When the old woman wanted to know if everything was fixed up, he just nodded his head. Then they all set there, and nobody said a word for a long time.

Finally the old woman couldn't stand it no longer. "Did you see pappy?" she asked. The brother-in-law didn't return no answer at first, but after while he says, "Yeah." The old woman waited awhile, and then she says, "You sure it was him?" The brother-in-law set there a long time, and spit in the fire, but finally he answered, "Yeah." Anybody could see he didn't feel like talking about it no more, but pretty soon the old woman spoke up and says, "How did pappy look?" The brother-in-law thought things over about five minutes, and then he took another drink. "Porely," says he.

A fellow hadn't ought to laugh about things like that, because it looks like you ain't got no respect for the dead. But the story got around, and lots of folks thought it was downright comical.

YOCUM USED HIS HEAD

ONE TIME there was a fellow named Clyde Yocum, that lived up the river. Clyde couldn't read nor write, but he had a good head on his shoulders. Book-learning didn't amount to much in them days, because everybody hunted and trapped for a living. The facts of the matter is, Clyde Yocum was just about the smartest man in this country. A fellow like that was respected and looked up to, just like a senator or a big doctor is now.

The boys used to tell how Clyde drawed a bead on a nice fat deer, when all of a sudden he seen a panther a-sneaking through the cedar brakes. There wasn't no repeating guns in them days, just single shot rifles, and a muzzle-loader at that. Clyde wanted to kill the panther, but he needed the deer too, because his family was hollering for venison. If he shot the panther, the deer would be a mile off before he could load. But if he shot the deer, the panther would have him in a bad spot, because it ain't safe to fool with panthers when your gun's empty. And even if the panther didn't jump on Clyde, the varmint might grab the deer and run off with it.

Lots of fellows would have got excited, but Clyde just stood there cool as a cucumber, trying to figure out what he better do. The panther seen the deer all right, but he didn't see Clyde. The deer didn't see Clyde or the panther either one, and couldn't smell 'em because the wind was blowing the other way. Clyde Yocum knowed what was going to happen, so he just stood still and waited.

The old panther moved up mighty slow, and pretty soon the

end of his tail begun to wiggle. Then all of a sudden he give a big jump, and caught the deer. Quick as a flash he bit through the deer's neck and killed it. Clyde never moved a muscle, but the panther must have caught the scent, because he begun to look around kind of uneasy. It was too late, though. Soon as Clyde seen the deer was dead he pulled the trigger, and shot the old panther right through the head.

That's the way the boys used to tell the story, and Clyde never did deny it. He was a man that didn't talk much, but nobody else in this country ever done such a trick as that. The smartest fellows we got nowadays would look like a half-wit, if you stacked 'em up alongside of Clyde Yocum.

A PICKARD NEVER FORGETS

ONE TIME there was a fellow named Jim Pickard, and three fellows from Joplin played a joke on him. That was a good many years ago, and them fellows had likely forgot all about it. But a Pickard never forgets anything, and he was bound to pay 'em back with interest, no matter how long it took.

So when these three fellows wanted to go rabbit hunting, Jim shook hands and offered to take 'em out in his new buggy. And pretty soon Jim happened to remark that he had bought the old Sanders farm, and the woodlot is full of brush. "I been intending to burn it off," says he, "and this is a good day to do it." And then he told them fellows to stand inside the fence, next to the orchard. "I'll set the brush afire," says he, "and all you got to do is shoot the rabbits when they run out." And they done just as he said.

They was a-shooting rabbits like it was a regular battle, when all of a sudden here come old man Sanders a-horseback. "What the hell do you fellows mean, setting my farm afire?" says he. The three fellows tried to tell him how Jim Pickard done it, but when they went down the road to see Jim, he wasn't there. Old man Sanders figured the whole thing was a lie, so he out with his shooting-pistol and took their guns. Then he made 'em walk all the way to town, with him riding behind a-threatening bloody murder at every step. He marched them fellows straight to the jail house, and the constable locked them up.

All three of them fellows kept a-hollering about Jim Pickard, so along that evening the constable asked Jim to come over. Jim looked at the prisoners through the bars. "They ain't no friends of mine," says he. "I never seen them before in my life." At that the three fellows begun to cuss worse than ever, and Jim stepped up close to look again. "Maybe I have seen them before," he says, "a long time ago." And pretty soon he says it was at the Baxter Springs reunion in 1904. "They was young then, not fat and bald-headed. But I believe they're the same fellows that put a bur under my saddle!" And then Jim says it ain't no surprise to him that they turned out to be desperate criminals, and probably there is big rewards for 'em all over the country.

The constable wouldn't pay no attention to anything them fellows said after that, so they had to stay in jail all night. Next morning Doc Holton identified all three, and fixed it up with old man Sanders, so the sheriff finally turned 'em loose. But that rabbit hunt cost them considerable money, and the boys around Joplin never did get done laughing about it.

"I like a joke as well as the next man," says Jim Pickard.

"But if anybody figures they can put a bur under my saddle, so I get throwed higher'n a kite right in front of the grandstand, they better think twice before they do it again," he says.

THE CHILI KING

ONE TIME there was a boy named Sid Connor that lived in one of them little shikepoke towns, and he had kind of a hard time. His folks was ornery, and they didn't have no money. The other boys made fun of Sid a good deal, and the merchants wouldn't give him no job. And then he wanted to go with the lawyer's daughter, but she just laughed because his hair wasn't cut right. Sid was pretty near growed up by that time, so he just walked out of town. He says to himself, "I will be a rich man some day, and then I will show these son-of-a-bitches." Next day he hopped a ride on the railroad cars, and just kept a-going till they come to Kansas City.

Well sir, that boy got a job washing dishes in a restaurant, and they give him two meals every day. Some folks let him sleep in a woodshed, and a man give him some old clothes. Sid would not buy nothing, but just saved every penny he got a hold of, and put it in the bank. And so it only took ten years till he had enough to start a little chili shack, and then he begun to make money a lot faster. The other young fellows in Kansas City used to wear good clothes and play pool and go to shows and drink beer and smoke cigars, and they would buy a dish of ice-cream whenever they felt like it. But Sid never done any of them things. He never even bought a newspaper all the time he lived in Kansas City, because a paper cost three cents, and it is better to save the three cents and invest it in the chili business. And all the time Sid was thinking how some day he would be a rich man, so then he could go back home and show them son-of-a-bitches.

After he worked twenty-five years that boy owned three fine chili parlors, and he was making lots of money. The big sign says: SID CONNOR, THE CHILI KING. But he still worked fifteen hours a day, and he never spent a nickel only for the business. He didn't eat nothing but chili beans, and he still wore old clothes that people give him, and he never even drunk one glass of beer. There was a pretty girl that liked him and she wanted to get married, but Sid kept thinking how much it would cost to keep a wife and have lace curtains and everything, so he give her the boot. The main thing was to be a rich man some day, so he could show them son-of-a-bitches back home.

Finally the day come when Sid Connor was a rich man sure enough, but he was pretty old by that time, and kind of sick besides. Sid bought some good clothes and a fine big car, and hired a man to run the car, because he never learned to drive. So then he went back to his old home town, and stayed at the new hotel. But there wasn't nobody in town that ever heard of the Connor family. Sid went to look for them big merchants that wouldn't give him a job, but their stores was all tore down, and the folks didn't even remember their name. The lawyer's daughter that giggled about his haircut had been gone pretty near thirty years, because Sid found her little stone in the graveyard. Every one of them people that laughed at him was dead, or else they moved away a long while ago.

Soon as he seen how things was, the Chili King got in his big car and went back to Kansas City. But he never did amount to much after that. He throwed two or three big parties, and give most of his money to them floozies that hung around the restaurant. The lawyers got a big slice, of course, and he left the rest of it to the nurse that took care of him in the hospital. And then one morning old man Connor was dead, so that's the end of the story.

TURTLES GROW FAST

ONE TIME there was a fellow named Doc that run a drugstore, and he was a great joker. His wife had a fine glass bowl in the setting room, with some green moss in the water. And then a boy give her a little turtle about as big as a silver dollar, with red and yellow stripes on it. Doc says, "It sure is pretty, but that kind of turtles grow awful fast, and you will have to buy a bigger bowl." "Nonsense," says his wife, "old lady Howard has got a turtle like that in her goldfish globe, and it ain't growed a bit in three years."

All them fishermen was friendly with Doc, and he passed the word around that he was buying turtles with red and yellow stripes on 'em. "Bring 'em to the back of my store," says he, "but don't say nothing about it." Pretty soon Doc had all different sizes of turtles, and he kept 'em in a tub back of the store. So then one night he took his wife's turtle out of the bowl, and put in another one that was about a half inch bigger. Next night he done the same thing again. Doc's wife seen that the turtle had growed some, but she never said nothing. Three nights after that, Doc changed turtles again. Doc's wife told old lady Howard that the turtle was a-growing mighty fast. But the old lady says it can't be, because she knows all about turtles from the ground up, and they don't grow a bit in three years.

Doc waited a couple of nights before he traded again, and this time the turtle was so much bigger that his wife hollered out loud when she seen it. Pretty soon old lady Howard come over. "There ain't no doubt about it," says Doc's wife, "that turtle has growed four inches in seven days." The old lady just set there goggle-eyed. Some neighbor women come over to look at it, and they all said they never heard tell of such a thing.

Next time he made the switch Doc put in a regular old gollywhopper of a turtle, so big it wouldn't hardly go in the bowl. Doc's wife run out and fetched old lady Howard. The old woman just took one look, and then she set down and begun to fan herself. "That ain't no natural turtle," says she. "There's something terrible wrong here, and maybe it's witch's work. You better get your husband to kill the beast." With that old lady Howard walked out of the house, and she wouldn't come back no more until the turtle was got rid of.

The whole business upset Doc's wife considerable, but when she told Doc about it he just laughed. "I told you it was one of them fast growing cooters," says he. So next day Doc took the big turtle down to the store, and brought home the little one about the size of a dollar. Doc's wife watched it kind of uneasy all summer, but the critter never growed a bit. "A turtle is a fine pet to keep in fish bowls," she says. "The main thing is, to be careful you don't get one of the fast growing kind."

THE BOLSTER

ONE TIME there was some folks had a lot of company all at once, and the house was pretty crowded. After they got everybody settled down for the night there was one boy and one girl left over, so they had to put 'em in the same bed. It ain't so bad as you might think, because they was in a big room with a lot of beds, and grown folks a-sleeping all around 'em. Just for the looks of the thing, the old woman put an old-fashioned bolster in the middle of the bed. A bolster is like a big long pillow, but stuffed a lot harder than common pillows are nowadays.

The boy didn't get to sleep for a long time, because he was thinking about the pretty girl in bed with him. He knowed the girl was awake too, but there wasn't nothing he could do about it. The moon was a-shining right in onto the bed, and there was all them people right in the same room. Also the boy hadn't never seen the girl until that day, and didn't know what kind of a girl she was, or how she was going to act. He didn't want to raise no disturbance, and maybe get throwed right out of the house. So the boy just laid there, and finally he went to sleep.

When he woke up next morning the womenfolks was all dressed, and they was cooking breakfast. The girl acted pleasant enough, but she didn't talk much. Along that evening him and her went a-walking down by the spring branch, and they come to a fence without no gate in sight. "I can jump over easy enough," says the girl, "but I'm afraid you'll have to go round." The boy just stared at her. "What are you talking about?" he says. The girl kind of giggled. "Well," says she, "a fellow that can't climb over a bolster ain't going to have much luck with a five-rail fence."

The story don't say what the boy done after that, but it ain't hard to guess. Him and her didn't get back to the house till pretty late, anyhow.

IDA STREET'S BYWORD

ONE TIME there was a man named Street, and folks said he was henpecked, because his wife was always giving him orders what to do. She was a good Christian woman, but whenever things went wrong she would holler "Hell's fuzzy!" loud as she could. There wasn't nobody else in the country that hollered "Hell's fuzzy!" like that, so it was knowed for miles around as Ida Street's byword.

When Ida died old man Street felt pretty bad, and he missed her something terrible. But it wasn't no time till he got to cavorting round amongst the womenfolks. And then he kind of simmered down on a young grass widow that lived up the road a piece. One night him and her was walking home from a pie supper, and they had to pass the graveyard where Ida was buried. Just as they got even with the gate both of 'em heard a kind of *whing-whing-whing,* and here come something across the road. It looked like a woman with a long white dress on, a-floating about ten foot above the ground. Then they heard somebody holler, "Hell's fuzzy! You must have went cra-a-a-zy!" just like that.

Them two just stood still for a second, and then they took out. Old man Street had hold of the woman's hand at first, but she couldn't keep up with him. So he turned loose, and left her to get home the best she could. The grass widow pulled up her dress and run like a quarter horse, but the old man was away ahead. She hollered bloody murder at every jump, but old man Street was saving his breath to grunt with. He run plumb into town, and stayed at the hotel all night, because he was scared to go home. The hotel people said he never turned out the lamp till it was broad daylight, and the birds a-singing in the trees.

About a week after that the boys went and told the old man how the whole thing was a joke. The ghost wasn't nothing but a dummy dressed in a nightgown, that they strung on a wire and pulled across the road with a kite string. The screw-eye running on the wire made the *whing-whing-whing* noise. And the voice was just Jim Beasley a-hollering from where he was hid under a bush. Old man Street shook his head. He says it is a sin to mock the dead, and anybody that done such a thing will suffer for it some day. "You just wait and see if I ain't right," says he.

It might be that old man Street never did believe what them boys told him. "Hell's fuzzy!" was still a-ringing in his ears. He knowed Ida's byword better than anybody, and it sure don't sound like Jim Beasley a-hollering, he says. The old man just kind of stayed around the hotel all summer, and plumb give up running after grass widows. Nobody ever seen him go past the graveyard of a night, neither.

TOM AND JERRY

ONE TIME there was two oxen named Tom and Jerry. They was pulling a plow, and the ground was full of big old roots. It was hard work, but the farmer fed pretty good. While Tom and Jerry was eating that night, Tom kept a-grumbling. "You and me are working ourself to death," says he. "I'm going to let on like I am sick, and get some rest." Jerry studied awhile, and then he says, "Tom, it won't do no good. You better just stick to your plowing."

Next morning Tom just laid in the barn and groaned, but Jerry went to work the same as always. Tom took it easy all day, while Jerry had to pull the plow by himself. That night Tom was a-feeling fine, and he says he is going to play off sick again tomorrow. Jerry was awful tired, but he says, "Well, you do whatever you want. But I'm afraid you're making a bad mistake."

Tom let on like he was sick for three days a-running. He just took it easy all day, while Jerry had to pull the plow by himself. Finally Jerry says, "Tom, I heard the farmer talking today, and he figures on selling you." Tom just laughed. "Nobody is going to buy an ox that is sick," says he. "And it is all right with me anyhow, because there ain't nobody works any harder than the farmer that owns us now." Jerry didn't say no more, but he seen that Tom was a-riding for a fall.

There was a stranger come around next morning, and Tom just laid down and groaned like he was sick. But pretty soon he heard the folks a-talking, and they said the stranger run a butcher shop in Durgenville. Soon as he heard that, Tom jumped up and run around to show how healthy he was, but it didn't do no good. The farmer figured the best medicine for a sick ox is a quick sale. It wasn't no time at all till the butcher led poor Tom off down the road. The children was all a-crying, because they knowed he was headed for the slaughter house.

Jerry seen right from the start that Tom was a blowed-up sucker, but there wasn't nothing to be done. When a fellow once gets it in his head that he can live without work, there ain't no use talking to him.

WILD PIGEONS

ONE TIME there was some fellows started to sail across the sea in a big ship. There wasn't no engine in the ship, they just had sails to catch the wind. When the wind died down the ship wouldn't go, so they just waited till the wind started blowing again. It took a long time to sail across the ocean in them days.

The ship had got about half way across when the wind quit blowing, so the sailors didn't have nothing to do. They just set around and played cards mostly. The people was not worried, because they had barrels of good water to drink, and plenty of salt meat and potatoes. They had wine and whiskey too, so everybody figured they was doing all right. One day there was a lot of birds come along, and some of them lit down on the ship. They was wild pigeons, just like them big flocks we used to see back home. The pigeons was so tired they couldn't fly no more, and the sailors killed 'em with sticks. The boys was glad to get them pigeons, as it would

103

be a change from rusty old pork all the time. The cook made a fine pie out of dried apples to go with the dinner. And one fellow says it is good luck, because God must have sent them pigeons so we could have something better to eat.

Next morning here come a lot more pigeons, and they lit on the ship. The sailors took sticks and killed all they wanted. But the pigeons just kept a-coming till the air was full of 'em, and you couldn't hardly see the sun. The whole ship was covered with feathers and blood and bird manure all over everything. The sailors was killing pigeons fast as they could, and throwing 'em in the sea. Everybody on the ship was up to their waist in pigeons, and finally one fellow fired off the little brass cannon. A lot of pigeons flew up in the air for a minute, but they come right back. Them pigeons was so wore out they couldn't fly no further. They had to roost on the ship because it was out in the middle of the ocean, and there wasn't no other place for them to light.

The fellows on the ship seen they was in a bad fix. They all begun to shoot off guns and rockets, and some built fires to smoke the pigeons away. But the pigeons just kept a-piling up till the ship turned over on one side, and a lot of water rolled in. Some of the sailors tried to get off in a little boat with oars, but it didn't do no good. The pigeons just piled up on the little boat like bees a-swarming, and sunk the whole business. Just before dark the ship tipped over again, and took in a lot more water. When morning come the ship was plumb gone. There wasn't nothing left but a few big timbers, and a lot of boxes and barrels a-floating around.

The fellows that was on the ship all got drowned except one. A steamboat come along and the people seen this fellow a-floating because he had a cork jacket on, and he was holding onto a board besides. He had eat some dead pigeons but didn't have no water, because the water in the sea is too salty. The people in the steamboat picked him up and give him some water. But they couldn't understand what he said very good, because they was all foreigners. So when he told 'em what happened they thought the poor fellow must be crazy, because everybody knows that birds couldn't sink a ship, even if they was big as cows. And the captain of the steamboat says it is one of them Yankee lies, so then the fellow knocked the captain flat down. He says, "No man can call me a Yankee, because I was born in Arkansas and my mother was a lady." After he done that, they put big iron handcuffs on him.

It was two years before that fellow got back to Little Rock, and lots of the home folks didn't believe his story neither. Because they knowed that wild pigeons don't go no place only to eat acorns, and it ain't likely that pigeons would be flying over the sea, because there ain't no oak trees there. But after while everybody seen that the pigeons was all gone, and nobody could find out what become of 'em. So maybe they did fly out over the ocean and got drownded, like the fellow says.

There is several people right here in Arkansas that knowed that sailor well, and they can tell you all about him. But you better not write his name down in no book, because some of the kinfolks is still alive, and they wouldn't like it.

SAM FENTON WAS TEMPTED

ONE TIME Sam Fenton was a-setting on his porch, and it was raining cats and dogs. A stranger come along, all dressed up like a preacher in rutting season. "Hello,

Josh," says he, "where does Judge Ford live?" Sam didn't return no answer, so the foreigner hollered louder, like he thought the old man must be hard of hearing. "How did you know my name is Josh?" says Sam. "Oh, I just guessed it," answered the stranger. "Well, you just guess where Judge Ford lives at, then," says Sam Fenton.

The fellow gulped a couple of times. "All right, I give up," says he, "what might your name be?" Sam thought awhile. "It might be James Woodson Pendergast, but it ain't," he says. "Never mind, I don't care what your name is," says the stranger. "Do you know Judge Ford?" Sam thought about it a long time, and then he says, "No, I never heard tell of him." The stranger thought it was mighty funny, because Judge Ford has lived here fifteen years. "Yeah, I heard there was some newcomers moved in lately," says Sam Fenton.

"Newcomers!" says the stranger. "How long have *you* lived in this God-forsaken place?" Sam allowed that he's been here ever since the courthouse was built. "Well, when did they build the courthouse?" says the stranger. "You mean the old courthouse, or the new one?" says Sam. "Whichever courthouse you're talking about," the stranger says. "Oh, that one," says Sam, "why, they built it the same year I was born." The foreigner scowled worse than ever, and he says, "Have you lived here all your life?" Sam made out like he was feeling his pulse. "No," says he, "not yet."

"Listen, Josh," says the stranger, "we don't seem to be getting anywhere." Sam says he's satisfied to stay right here till after the election, but the foreigner ain't satisfied by no means. "Can't you see I'm wet to the skin?" Sam looked him over careful. "You must have been out in the rain," he says. "I'm hungry, too!" hollered the stranger. Sam thought this

106

over awhile. "Maybe you don't eat enough, and that's what caused it," says he. The stranger was kind of upset, but he seen there wasn't no use talking to Sam. "Tell me the shortest way back to town, and I won't trouble you any farther," he says.

"Just follow the ridge road a piece," says Sam, "till you see a plain cowtrail a-running to the left between two lightning-struck blackjacks, the other side of a little branch. Well, don't go that way! Take the righthand prong and push straight ahead till you hear kids a-hollering—that's the mouth of Schoolhouse Draw. Soon as you get past them children, turn south across old man Price's bottom. Be sure and shut both gates, and look out for a red bull. There ain't no road after you pass Price's but you just kind of ford the creek endways, and it'll fetch you out somewheres near what is knowed as the Harrycane Brakes, and then—" The stranger busted in right there, and says it sounds kind of complicated. Sam thought awhile, and then he allowed maybe the stranger is right. "If it was me going to town," says Sam, "I wouldn't start from here at all."

The foreigner just looked at Sam a minute, and then he says, "I believe you're a damned fool!" Sam went right ahead lighting his pipe. "Maybe so, stranger," says he. "But I ain't wet, and I ain't lost, and I ain't hungry."

The stranger was pretty mad by this time, as he seen Sam was getting the best of him. "What kind of a man are you, anyhow?" says he. "I'm a Democrat," answered Sam. "I don't mean that! To hell with your politics!" the foreigner hollered. Sam Fenton got up mighty solemn. "Mister," says he, "are you a *Republican?*" The fellow didn't make no answer, but he looked the guiltiest you ever seen. "My God, right in my own front yard," says Sam, like he was plumb horrified. And then he yelled for the old woman. "Lucy, fetch me the shot-gun!" And with that the stranger took off down the road, a-splashing water at every jump.

Lucy come to the door just in time to see the foreigner out of sight. "You ought to be ashamed," she says. "I couldn't help it, Lucy," says Sam, "that fellow tempted me beyond my strength. He ain't hurt none, just a little muddy. And think what a story he'll tell the folks back in Illinois, or wherever it was he come from!" And Sam Fenton set there and laughed till the tears run down his face.

PLUMBING IN OKLAHOMA

ONE TIME the wildcatters was drilling in Oklahoma, and all of a sudden the oil come in, so a lot of poor folks got rich over night. The first thing they done was to buy new boots and big automobiles, of course. But the money still kept a-rolling in, so everybody begun to build fine big houses. Some people that didn't even have a privy six months ago was living in regular mansions now, with three or four fancy bathrooms.

There was a fellow come along that had done some pipe-fitting on windmills out West, so he told them rich folks he was a expert plumber, and they give him the contract to put fine bathrooms in several new houses. Oklahoma was kind of careless then, and a plumber didn't need no license. He got along surprising good, for a fellow that hadn't never done no plumbing before. The bank give him plenty of credit, and he shipped in the best fixtures that money could buy. He was a very smart fellow, and he kind of learned the trade as he went along.

The first big house that he done the plumbing for, everything worked fine only he got the pipes mixed up, so the toilet was running with hot water instead of cold water. When the rich woman seen steam coming out of the toilet she set up quite a holler. But the plumber was a good talker. "Why, ma'am," says he, "you told me to use the best of everything. I thought of course you wanted Hollywood toilets." And he says all the big movie stars use hot-water stools in their bathrooms nowadays, and the wealthy people in New York have all switched over to Hollywood toilets, because hot water absorbs every bit of offensive odor. Also just think how comfortable it is to have warm vapor a-rising up, instead of ice cold air which would freeze the tail off a brass monkey, he says. So then the plumber begun to talk about Mable Normand and John D. Rockefeller and Mary Pickford and Helen Walker and J. Pierpont Morgan and Gloria Swanson and Wallie Reid and Douglas Fairbanks. It wasn't no time at all till the woman seen the advantages of having hot water to flush the toilets.

She told the other rich people about it too, and pretty soon they was all hollering for hot water toilets. And there was one big house with four bathrooms where the plumbing was already put in. The man that owned the house made the plumber take the pipes out and fix it so the stools run with hot water, because expense is no object and I don't want nothing but the very best, he says.

It all happened several years ago, and things is different now, because the people are educated up to modern houses, of course. The bathrooms in them oil towns ain't no different from what they got in Kansas City, or even St. Louis. The

109

smart-aleck plumber went to Texas, and God only knows what become of him by this time. But the old settlers still josh each other sometimes about them Hollywood toilets, and they all say that plumber was the best talker of anybody in Oklahoma.

THREE SILVER LEGS

ONE TIME there was a girl up on Honey Creek got something the matter with her, and she couldn't walk a step. The girl looked just as healthy as ever, but she had to lay in bed all day long. The folks give her a whole bottle of medicine, but it didn't do no good. Doc Holton says he can't find nothing wrong with her legs, only she is paralyzed. He told 'em she might get well all of a sudden, or else maybe she would just stay like that. After Doc went back to town old Gram French come over, and Gram says somebody has planted bad feathers in the path. What she meant was, that an Indian woman throwed a spell on the girl's legs.

The folks didn't believe much in things like that, but finally they give Gram two dollars. Just before midnight she got to muttering charms, but nobody couldn't understand what Gram said only the Devil and his helpers. When the clock struck twelve she opened the door, and then she begun to knock on the bed with her left hand. Pretty soon there come a answer away off in the woods, and it went *tum-tiddy-um-tum* like them drums the Indians use at rain dances.

The girl on the bed begun to groan something terrible and the drums away off in the woods kept right on going *tum-tiddy-um-tum*. And here come something a-marching out from

110

under the bed, and it was a little black soldier about fourteen inches high, with three silver legs. The little black soldier was carrying a thing like a gun, but it wasn't no gun. You wouldn't believe it, only if you seen the thing with your own eyes.

The drums away off in the woods kept a-going *tum-tiddy-um-tum,* and the little black soldier kept on a-marching. The folks just set there goggle-eyed. Finally the little black soldier marched right out the door, and a big log in the fireplace broke in two so it fell on the hearth stone. Gram got up and shut the door. Pretty soon she lit the lamp, and the girl in the bed begun to kick with her legs. It wasn't no time at all till that girl was walking around the house just as lively as anybody.

Doc Holton come out to see her next day, and he says "Well, didn't I tell you she might get well all of a sudden?" The folks never said nothing to Doc about the drums and the little black soldier, or what the little black soldier was a-carrying, neither. Doc didn't believe in such as that. It's one of them things you wouldn't believe yourself, only if you seen it with your own eyes.

CAN RATS READ?

ONE TIME there was an old man come through the settlement afoot. His clothes was kind of ragged, with a funny looking hat on his head. So when he went past the old Ragsdale place, that big boy with the buck teeth throwed some wet corncobs at him. The old man seen who was a-throwing them cobs, but he just kept on walking down the road.

When the old man come to Bud Henderson's house, he stopped to get a drink of water. Him and Bud got to talking, and pretty soon Sally Henderson cooked up a good supper, with hot cornbread and fried meat. It was the first victuals the old man had eat that day, and he drunk three cups of coffee. While they was eating a big rat run across the floor, and Sally says, "The rats is the worst I ever seen." After supper they set out on the porch awhile, and then Bud says there is a extra bed and the old man better stay with them all night. And so he done it.

Next morning Sally give the old man a fine breakfast, and he says, "You folks sure have treated me right, so I am going to get rid of them rats for you. All you got to do is give me a pencil and a piece of paper." And also, he says, "What is the name of them people down the road where they got a big boy with buck teeth?" Sally says their name is Ragsdale, but they are a kind of mean family, so her and Bud don't have no truck with them. The old man set down and wrote a letter like this:

DEAR MISTER RAT you have been here a long time and wore out your welcome, these folks are fixing to concrete the cellar and build a new corncrib very tight, so you will not get much to eat from now on, and they are going to put out poison besides. You better take all your kinfolks and move over to Ragsdale's place with a red roof only a quarter mile down the road. Because there is lots of corn and a smokehouse full of meat and a big cellar with all kind of vegetables laying around. You will be happy there, and you can live right under the kitchen, as the Ragsdales haven't got no cats, and there is only one dog very old and pretty near blind. This is the truth as you can ask the rats in town because they all know me, and I would not fool you. A FRIEND TO RATS.

He wrapped the letter around a raw potato and stuck it down a hole in the floor. Then he wrote another letter and wrapped it around a ear of corn and throwed it under the barn. And then he wrote another letter and wrapped it around a slice of bacon and put it under the smokehouse. "Well, in three days the rats will all be gone, and they will be better off at Ragsdale's anyhow," he says. "And that big boy with the buck teeth better think twice before he throws some more wet cobs at people." And with that the old man picked up his little satchel and walked on down the road.

Bud and Sally didn't say nothing till the old man was out of sight, and then they had to laugh. Sally says, "Well, I have heard about conjuring rats, but I never seen it done before." And Bud says, "It is all foolishness, because everybody knows rats can't read writing, and them old-timers sure have got some funny notions," he says. Sally just laughed, and she says, "Well, he is a nice old man anyhow, and I'm glad we give him some hot victuals and a bed to sleep in for a change." Bud says he is glad too, and then they never thought no more about it.

It was about a week after that when Sally says, "Bud, have you seen any rats lately?" Bud looked kind of funny, and finally he says, "No, I ain't." So then both of them watched careful, but they never seen no signs of a rat. And then they heard folks talking how the Ragsdales was just eat out of house and home with rats, and they was even jumping on the beds and biting the children of a night. The Ragsdale people tried cats and traps and poison, but it didn't seem to do no good.

Bud and Sally never did talk much about the rat conjure, and Bud still says he don't believe no rat could read them

113

letters. But there ain't no rats at Henderson's to this day, and the Ragsdale place is just a-swarming with 'em. Maybe it is because Bud and Sally always treat everybody right, instead of throwing cobs at old men that come down the road.

THE PAPER SALESMAN

ONE TIME there was a fellow named Remington running a store at Beaver Springs, and he had a big stock of general mechandise. When the tourists begun to come down here in the summer time they bought all their stuff at the store, and Remington done so good he hired a young fellow to wait on the customers. The young fellow's name was Elmer, and he didn't have much sense. He worked hard and tried to learn the business, though. Elmer figured maybe some day he would have a store of his own.

A woman come in the store and she wanted some powdered sugar, but Elmer didn't know nothing about powdered sugar. So he says, "No, ma'am, we haven't got no powdered sugar," and then the woman went out.

Old man Remington was in the back room, and pretty soon he says, "Elmer, if a customer wants powdered sugar and we ain't got none, you ought to sell her something else." Elmer thought about it awhile, and scratched himself. "You mean I should show her the J. & P. Coates crochet-thread, or some new oil-pack sardines?" he says. "Hell no," says old man Remington, "don't never get smart with the customers. Just tell her we're fresh out of powdered sugar, but we got fine granulated sugar, and maple sugar in cakes, and clarified brown sugar too, the best you ever tasted. And if she don't buy nothing you say 'thank-you-ma'am' anyhow, and tell her we'll order some powdered sugar when the drummer comes from Joplin on Wednesday."

Elmer was still thinking about powdered sugar when Judge Decker's wife come in, and she wanted six rolls of toilet paper. It just happened that the tourists had bought the last of the toilet paper. "I'm sorry, ma'am," says Elmer, "we're fresh out of that. But we got wallpaper, and wrapping paper, and waxed paper, and paper napkins, and the biggest ten-cent tablets you ever seen." Judge Decker's wife just looked at Elmer like she thought he had went crazy. "We got sand-paper too, ma'am. And flypaper—" Judge Decker's wife looked plumb horrified. "Sandpaper! Flypaper!" she says, and then she turned around and marched out of there.

So far as anybody knows, Elmer never did say nothing about the time he tried to sell flypaper to Judge Decker's wife. But the story got around amongst the womenfolks, and some of the young ones would laugh right in Elmer's face, whenever they come in the store.

HE TALKED KIND OF SLOW

ONE TIME there was a fellow named Jerry Blakemore that never done anything in a hurry. He wasn't what you would call dumb, but just kind of deliberate. The folks used to tell lots of stories about Jerry, and there was several boys in town that could talk just exactly like him.

Furs was bringing good money in them days, so the folks done a lot of night hunting on Greasy Creek. Soon as the dogs treed, Jerry would climb up and shake down the coon. It was a dark night, and they didn't have only one old lantern, so you couldn't see nothing overhead. Pretty soon the boys heard a lot of scuffling and growling in the treetop. After while Jerry sung out, "This . . . here . . . coon . . . is a-biting . . . me." One of the fellows on the ground hollered, "Choke him, Jerry, choke him!" The coon kept on a-growling. Finally Jerry says, "I . . . am . . . a-choking . . . him. . . . The . . . harder . . . I . . . choke . . . him . . . the . . . worser . . . he . . . bites."

Another time there was a drummer hired Jerry to take him up on Bear Creek. Jerry was driving a old Ford, and they took the river road. The streams was up, and the road was terrible narrow and slippery. The salesman kept a-chattering about this and that, because he didn't think there was no danger. But Jerry knowed better, and he was driving mighty careful. Finally he spoke up, "I . . . believe . . . she's a-going . . . to . . ." Just then the flivver skidded off the muddy road, and went plumb out of sight in the deep water. The drummer tore loose and come a-sputtering to the top. Then Jerry come up beside him, and spit out a quart of creek water. "A-going . . . to . . . turn . . . over," says Jerry.

They used to tell about how old man Blankenship killed himself, and Jerry went to break the news to the widow. He just set there a long time, and finally he says, "We . . . found . . . your . . . old . . . man." Old lady Blankenship looked cheerful enough, and she says, "Where did you find him?" Jerry acted kind of uneasy. "A-hanging . . . in . . . the . . . barn," says he. Old lady Blankenship thought about it awhile, and then she says, "Did you cut him down?" Jerry just shook his head. "Why didn't you cut him down?"

says the old woman. "He . . . wasn't . . . dead . . . yet,"
says Jerry.

Some of the stories them boys used to tell was true, but
most of them was just made-up tales. They was all funny,
though, to anybody that knowed Jerry Blakemore.

THEM DRUNKEN PAINTERS

ONE TIME there was a fellow come into
town with a load of pumpkins. We had just got our new fire
department started then. There was a big brass fire engine,
with two fine black horses. The new hook-and-ladder wagon
was painted red, and they had a good team too. That outfit
cost the town a lot of money, and we was mighty proud of it. But
this farmer on the load of pumpkins didn't know much about
fire departments.

The fire bell started ringing just as he got to Fourth and
Main, and he pulled over to let the fire engine go by. But
then the damn fool started out in the middle of the street again,
so the hook-and-ladder wagon hit him from behind. It knocked
him galley west, and scattered pumpkins all over the south
end of town.

Next thing the farmer knowed he was in Doc Holton's
office, and Doc had him bandaged from head to foot. Soon
as the fellow could talk he begun to cuss the reckless son-of-a-
bitches that busted his wagon, and he says it's as much as a
man's life is worth to come into town nowadays. Doc says,
"Well, when our fire bell is a-ringing, people ought to get out
of the way, so the fire department can go by." The farmer
says he heard the bell all right, and pulled over to the side

117

of the road just like everybody else. "The fire engine didn't hit me," says he, "it was them drunken painters that come a-tearing along behind!"

THE SON OF A BISHOP

ONE TIME there was a young fellow named Asbury, and his daddy was a bishop in the Methodist church. They sent the boy to college back East somewheres, and then he wanted to be a congressman, so all the church people swarmed out to shell the woods for Jim Asbury. A politics committee went to every cabin on the creek, and finally they come to Seth Thompson's place. He was a smart old man, but so deef he couldn't hear himself thunder. Everybody had to take turns hollering into his ear-trumpet. Seth knowed it was about the election, but he couldn't make out who they wanted him to vote for.

The folks kept a-hollering "Jim Asbury! Jim Asbury!" till finally Seth got the name all right, but he didn't seem to know who Jim Asbury was. "He's the son of a bishop! Son of a bishop!" they yelled into the ear-trumpet. "Oh well, all them politicians is," says Seth. "How does he stand on evolution?"

Old Deacon Jones allowed that Jim was against evolution, and Seth promised to vote for him, so the committee called it a day. But them pious Methodists looked kind of red in the face, and some of the young folks giggled a little on the way back to town.

THE MAN THAT HATED BATS

ONE TIME there was a man named Fraser come from somewhere down in Arkansas. He was kind of a hatchet-faced fellow, with red hair. Everybody liked him, because he kept his mouth shut and tended to his own business. He knowed more about making whiskey than anybody in this country. It was the time when all Creation had went dry, and the folks in Joplin and Springfield would pay good money for most anything that had a kick in it. Pretty near everybody on White River was running stills in them days.

This Red Fraser knowed all the tricks, and he never got in no trouble. When them long-haired boys from the south end of the county tried to run over him, he made 'em hunt their holes. He wasn't afraid of the sheriff neither, and he knowed how to handle revenuers. There was just one funny thing about Red, and that is he wouldn't go in a cave, no matter what happened. Finally Shock Curtis found out that it wasn't caves he was scared of, it was bats. Whenever he seen a bat, Red would shake all over like a dog getting rid of a peach-stone.

"A bat ain't a natural bird," says he, "because birds lay eggs. Bats ain't animals neither, because natural animals can't fly. God made birds and God made animals, but who do you reckon made bats? Look a bat in the face, and you can see damnation plain as day! Look at a bat's wings, and see how the Devil travels round the world in seven minutes flat! The preachers can say whatever they want, but I believe bats is devils straight from Hell, and I don't want no truck with 'em." The caves in this country has mostly got bats in them, and that's the reason Red Fraser wouldn't work with no moon-shiner that done his cooking underground.

One Sunday the boys went down to the Mill Creek cave and caught five or six bats where they was a-hanging on the roof. They carried them bats in a flour sack, and turned 'em loose in the room where Red was a-sleeping. Then the boys hid in some brush, and throwed a rock against the shanty. Red woke up a-yelling like a steam whistle. The boys heard two shots, and out he come. He had an old thumb-buster forty-five in one hand, and his pants in the other. Over the hill he went, running barefooted on them sharp rocks, and never even looked back once.

Nobody around here ever seen Red Fraser again. The boys all hid out for two or three days, because they figured Red was so mad he might do something plumb desperate. It all kind of blowed over pretty soon, though. Some say that Red run all the way to Arkansas in one night, and him barefooted. Shock Curtis told it around that he joined the church, and took up farming somewhere down in Searcy county. Maybe so, but the folks never did find out for sure.

GOLD IS WHERE YOU FIND IT

ONE TIME there was an old man lived out east of town. Nobody knowed much about him, only he was part Choctaw, and had some kinfolks down in the Kiamichi country. Some folks said he used to be a gambler, but his gambling days was over a long time ago. Him and his wife

120

had a little garden, and kept a few chickens. They done all right till the old woman died, but it got kind of lonesome after that. Finally he decided to sell the farm, and go out West somewheres.

The trouble was that the price of land had went down, and the place wouldn't bring nowheres near what it was worth. Things went along for about a year, and the old man didn't have no money only what he got peddling eggs and chickens around town. One day he sold three live pullets to the real-estate fellow's wife. When she went to clean one of them she found something funny, and the real-estate man says, "Where did you get that?" so she told him out of the chicken's gizzard. He sent it off to a college somewhere, and that's how they found out it was a gold nugget.

Soon as he knowed it was sure enough solid gold, the real-estate fellow sent his boy out to buy some of the old man's chickens. He got four pullets this time, and when him and his wife cleaned them gizzards they found two more nuggets, bigger than the other one.

First thing in the morning the real-estate fellow drove out to the old man's place. He set on the porch awhile, and seen the chickens a-feeding up and down the spring branch. "I might buy this farm for a investment," says he, "if I could get it cheap enough." The old man says the banker has been out several times lately to buy chickens, so he thinks maybe the banker is going to buy the place. The real-estate fellow made a pretty good offer right then, but the old man says "There ain't no hurry, and maybe the banker will pay more money." The real-estate fellow bought a couple of chickens, and killed 'em the minute he got back home. And what do you think? Both of them chickens had solid gold in their gizzard!

121

The real-estate fellow and his wife set up pretty near all night a-talking. And next day he went out and bought the old man's farm. He paid a whopping big price, so the old man give him all the household stuff and throwed in the chickens to boot. And then the old man took the money and went to visit his kinfolks down in the Kiamichi country. The real-estate people killed all the chickens before the old man was hardly out of sight, but they didn't find no nuggets in their gizzard. They sifted sand all up and down the branch, and built wooden troughs with water running through out of a hose, but there wasn't no gold in the sand. Then they got hired men and dug big holes all over the place, but there wasn't no nuggets in the holes, neither. The whole bunch worked night and day for pretty near a month, and then they give up. The real-estate fellow says there ain't no gold on the place, and he says that old Choctaw scoundrel has swindled me out of my savings. Him and his wife got to fighting about who was to blame, and that was the end of the Sequoyah county gold rush.

About a year after that a couple of Briartown boys went deer hunting down on the Kiamichi, and they run across the old man that used to peddle chickens. He was living in a nice cabin, with a pretty little squaw to keep house for him. He says everything is hotsy-totsy now, and I have invested my money in government bonds. The boys asked the old man about the gold mine, but he says it was just a kind of joke. "There wasn't only six nuggets," says he, "just keepsakes I fetched home from the Klondike in '98. I picked out six of my best pullets, and they gobbled up that gold like it was corn. A man's got a right to feed his own chickens, ain't he?"

CRUELTY TO ANIMALS

ONE TIME there was a widow named Benson that bought the old Starbuck place, and built a fine new house, and dammed up the spring branch for a fishpond. They say she come from St. Louis, after her man died and left her a washtub full of money. She just bought whatever she wanted at the store for cash, and never done a lick of work. The home folks treated her the best they knowed how, but she didn't neighbor much with anybody. Her friends was all rich people from some big town. They come to see her every Saturday, and throwed big parties. You could hear them whooping and hollering over there all night long.

The Shackleton family lived down the road a piece, and they had a big old hound dog named Booster, that was always a-smelling round the Benson place. Sometimes he would chase one of them fancy long-haired cats. The widow woman didn't like dogs, and she throwed rocks at him. Finally she told old man Shackleton would he please keep Booster at home. The old man didn't say nothing, but everybody knows you can't tie up a good tree dog like that.

One Sunday they was having a big drunk party at Benson's, and old Booster come right up to the house a-sniffing around for something to eat. The widow begun to talk how the neighbors' dogs was a nuisance, and what is the best way to run them off? One of the city fellows made a big ball out of rags, and put coal oil on it. "Now," he says, "we will tie this on the dog with a string twenty foot long, so it won't get close enough to burn him. But it will scare the critter out of

123

a year's growth, and he won't hang around here no more," says the city fellow.

The string was so long that Booster didn't pay no mind at first, but when he seen that ball of fire was fastened to his tail he went plumb crazy. The city folks figured he would run down the road for home, but Booster crawled right under the widow woman's house, and drug that big ball of fire in after him. A minute later the string burnt off, so here come Booster out the other side, and he wasn't hurt a bit. But the ball of fire was still under the house, with big black smoke a-rolling up over the sills.

Soon as Booster come out from under the house he took off with his mouth wide open, but the city folks and the fire was making so much noise you couldn't tell if Booster was a-yelping or not. Some of them fellows throwed a few buckets of water, but it didn't do no good. About all they could do was drive them big automobiles back a little ways, and carry some clothes and stuff out of the house. The widow woman was hollering like a steam whistle, but her fine new house burnt plumb to the ground, and she didn't have no insurance.

The city fellows all went back to St. Louis that night, and they took the Widow Benson along with 'em. She was still yelling like a crazy woman. Old man Shackleton come down to look things over, but there wasn't nothing left but a big pile of hot coals, with two black chimneys a-sticking up. You could see part of her fine big stove where the kitchen used to be, and four iron beds a-standing, but everything else was burnt to ashes. "It just goes to show that city people better not come down here abusing folks' dogs," says old man Shackleton.

YOU AIN'T COMING BACK

ONE TIME there was a city fellow come through the country, pretending like he was just a tourist. He went wandering around kind of aimless, trying to get people to sing songs. Told them he was going to write a book about old-time music. He hung around the square dances too, and got mighty friendly with fiddlers and guitar players and banjo pickers. Everybody knows that a fiddler would rather drink moonshine whiskey than eat. The city fellow thought he was mighty smart, but the home folks knowed what he was after, all right. They called him the singing revenuer.

Things just kind of drifted along all summer, till finally the singing revenuer come across one of Tom Christy's boys away up on Goober Mountain. Soon as the howdies was over the fellow sung one of them fool songs, and then he wanted to talk about moonshine. "They tell me your pappy's running off a batch today," says he, but the boy never returned no answer. "If I knowed where the boys have got the still," says the revenuer, "I'd go up there and visit with 'em awhile." But Tom Christy's boy didn't have nothing to say.

Pretty soon the fellow come right out and offered the youngster five dollars to tell him where the still was at. Tom Christy's boy looked at him contemptuous. "Just go up the path, and turn left at the first fork," says he. "The still's under the bluff, right by the second pour-off." The revenuer hitched up his belt. "Give me the five dollars," says Tom Christy's boy. The fellow just kind of grinned. "I'll give you the money when I come back," says he. The boy just set there, a-looking

125

out over the valley. "Mister," says he, "if you go up to that still, you ain't never coming back."

The revenuer didn't say nothing, but you could see he was a-thinking mighty serious. Pretty soon he got up and walked down the trail towards the settlement. Tom Christy and his boys moved their contraption that night, but there wasn't no need of it. About a week after that, the singing revenuer found two or three stills down on Buffalo Creek. But nobody ever seen him fooling around Goober Mountain again.

THEY PRAYED TO THE SUN

ONE TIME there was a fat woman from back East come to our town, and she was plumb crazy about Indians. You know about half of the folks around here has got some Cherokee blood in 'em, but the fat woman wasn't interested in that. She wanted to see wild savages with feathers in their hair, and paint all over 'em besides. The folks tried to tell her that Indians don't wear feathers much, and they don't use no paint neither, only maybe after a man is dead they will put two or three little marks on his face to show what family he belongs to. But all this stuff about eagle feathers and warpaint is just for the stomp dances nowadays, or else the Wild West show. The truth is that Indians look just like anybody else.

The folks tried to tell her how it was, but the woman didn't pay them no mind at all. Finally she hired old Pete Goodeagle to take her over in the Nation where she could meet up with some regular Indians. They was gone about two weeks, and there was a bunch of Osages that come up the river to catch fish. You know how the squaws wade out in a riffle and pound up buckeye roots, and it makes the fish drunk so they come to the top. All the men have to do is gather up the big ones. And then they clean the fish and dry 'em on poles, to eat in the winter time.

The fat woman says it was wonderful how they could catch

so many fish without no seine, and she figured there was some kind of magic to it. She stayed at some people's house that lived on a hill, where she could see the Indian camp down by the river. She watched them Indians all day long, and wrote it all down how the Indians done everything. Pete Goodeagle thought the fat woman must be crazy, but she wasn't.

About a year after that the folks heard how the fat woman

was going around the country making speeches about her life with the wild Indians, and she give lectures on the Chautauqua too, and the Chautauqua people paid her big money. And finally she got it printed in a magazine. It was a pretty good story, only the Indians in the picture looked like Comanches instead of Osage, and they was wearing mighty peculiar moccasins. She told how the Indians catch fish, all right. Only she made it sound terrible spooky and mysterious, when everybody knows they just pound up buckeye roots.

It says in the magazine that the old men of the tribe come out at dawn every morning, and pray to the rising sun. The folks told Pete Goodeagle about that, and he laughed right in their face. "She seen the old men come out and face the east, all right. But she was too far off to see what they was a-doing." And Pete laughed some more. "What does every old man do, first thing in the morning? Them Osages has got bladders, just like anybody else," says Pete Goodeagle. "They didn't have no privy, and the old men walked toward the sun because there is a lot of sawtooth briars west of the camp."

It just goes to show that you can't believe nothing they print in the goddam papers, or the stories in magazines neither. Everybody knows that the Osages is mostly Missionary Baptists, or else they belong to the Moonhead Peyote church, which is a kind of Holy Rollers. No wonder the people back East have got some funny notions, if they read them fool newspapers and magazines all the time.

THE CROW THAT TALKED

ONE TIME there was a rich man that lived on a farm, and he only had one boy. The boy wouldn't do no work on the farm. He just set around all day, playing with a tame crow, so the old man says for him to go somewheres else. The boy took his crow and went to Kansas City. He was a big upstanding fellow with good clothes, and there was a pretty lady on Twelfth Street that liked him fine. She let the boy live at her house, and got him a nice job in the pool hall. He done all right in Kansas City, and bought him a big bird-cage to keep the pet crow in.

After while he wrote a letter home about a doctor that could split the crow's tongue and learn it to talk just like anybody else. The old man thought this would be a fine thing, so he sent the boy fifty dollars. The boy just laughed. The fifty dollars come in handy to buy him a gold watch with a big chain, like all them other fellows that hangs around Kansas City.

Pretty soon he wrote another letter home about how the crow can talk fine now, but for fifty dollars more the doctor will learn the crow how to read and write. The old man thought this would be a fine thing, so he sent the boy another fifty dollars. The boy just laughed some more, and the fifty dollars come in handy because he had found out how to play black-jack by this time.

Then all of a sudden the boy and the pretty lady was not getting along so good, and it looked like there would be hell to pay on Twelfth Street. So finally the boy just got on the train and went back home. The old man was glad to see him, but he wanted to hear the crow talk. The boy looked mighty solemn. "I had to kill the crow," says he. The old man begun to raise hell, but the boy just shook his head. "Come out to the barn where maw won't hear us," says he, "and I'll tell you how it happened."

When they got to the barn the boy says, "That crow kept a-hollering the same thing all the time, so I took and wrung his neck." The old man was pretty mad. "You didn't have no business to kill our valuable crow just for talking, which I spent a hundred dollars to get him educated," says he. "What did the crow say, anyhow?" The boy shook his head. "Just a big tale about how you topped the hired girl in the hayloft," says he. "I won't stand for no bird a-telling lies on my pappy."

The old man just stood there with his mouth open for a minute, and then he looked around kind of uneasy. "You done right, son," says he. "Learning birds to talk is against Nature, anyhow. Are you plumb sure that crow is dead?" The boy just nodded his head. So then they went back to the house for dinner, and never said nothing more about it.

JACK AND THE OLD WITCH

ONE TIME there was a pretty girl that got lost from her folks. She just walked down the road a-crying because it was cold, and she didn't have nothing to eat. Pretty soon she come to a house, and there was an old woman told her to come in by the fire, and give her something to eat. The old woman was a witch, but the pretty girl didn't know it. Soon as she eat the bread and milk, the pretty girl turned into a big cat. After that she had to stay there and do all the work. Pretty near every day the old woman would give her a whipping besides.

The pretty girl would be working for the old witch yet, only there was a boy named Jack come along. "My God, that's the biggest pussy I ever seen," says he. The cat kind of grinned. "I'm a pretty girl by rights," she says, "but I look this way

because the old witch has throwed a spell on me." Jack just stared at her, and then he says ain't there no way you can break the spell? "I can't do nothing," says the cat, "till somebody kills the old witch." Jack showed her his big long frog-sticker. "Anything to convenience a lady," he says, "and I'm the very man can do it, too." The cat says, "Maybe you can, at that. But put away the knife," she says, "because you got to kill her with this," and she fetched him a big old broom made out of mistletoe.

Pretty soon in come a thing like a baldface hornet only it was big as a calf, with a stinger two foot long. "That's her!" says the cat. So Jack beat the hornet to death with the broom, and swept it out of the house. "She'll be back," says the cat. Jack waited awhile, and here come a thing like a snake, only it was big as a barrel with a forked tongue two foot long. "That's her!" says the cat. So Jack beat the snake to death with the broom, and swept it out of the house. "She'll be back once more," says the cat. "If you kill her this time, the old witch is gone for good. But don't sweep the corpse out the door. I want to burn her plumb to ashes." So then the cat throwed a lot of wood in the fireplace.

Pretty soon Jack heard a noise outside, and in come a little black woman with a club two foot long. "That's her!" says the cat. The witch throwed the club, but Jack beat her to death with the broom, and swept the carcass into the fire. The thing popped and twisted and crackled and sizzled a long time. It come clear out on the hearth once, but Jack pushed the old devil back in the chimney and let her burn till there wasn't nothing left only ashes.

So then he looked around and the cat was gone, but there was the pretty girl a-standing right by the bed. She just grinned at Jack, and says, "Well, how do I look?" Jack says, "You look wonderful, and my head is spinning round like a top." The pretty girl laughed, and she says, "You better set down and rest while I fix us some supper." So that's what they done, and him and her got pretty well acquainted. One day the pretty girl says, "There's a lot of gold under the house, and it belongs to you because you are the one that killed the witch." "Well," says Jack, "I'll give you half of it." But she says, "I don't want no gold myself, all I need is a rich husband." So Jack and the pretty girl got married, and they lived happy ever after.

THE DEATH OF LITTLE JEMSON

ONE TIME there was a man lived in town and he got to be the postmaster. He had a lot of grown-up children, and he was a great fellow to play jokes. One of his boys in Kansas City sent the old man six fine neckties, but they was all black. So then the new schoolmarm from Joplin stopped at the postoffice, and she wanted to know how come he wore black neckties all the time here lately. "Little Jemson is dead," says he. And then the old man kind of turned away, like he just couldn't stand to talk about it. The schoolmarm says she didn't know little Jemson was dead, and she is mighty sorry to hear it.

The schoolmarm went on down the street, and pretty soon her and another woman got to talking. So then she says, "It's too bad about little Jemson, and the postmaster is all broke up." But the other woman didn't know who little Jemson was, and neither did the schoolmarm, because the postmaster has got so many children, and maybe one of his brothers was named Jemson for all she knows. Before sundown people all over town was talking about how little Jemson is dead. And there was some claimed they use to know him well, but the truth is nobody could remember a goddam thing about little Jemson.

Finally a woman says to the postmaster's wife how it is too

bad about little Jemson. The postmaster's wife just kind of choked up. And then she says, "Thanks for your sympathy and I sure do need it, because I'm married to the damndest clown that ever walked this earth!" And then she just laughed till the tears run down her face, and they couldn't get another word out of her. Everybody thought it was a mighty funny way to act, when there was a death in the family. And some folks told it around that Jemson got in trouble years ago, and now he has died in prison, so it is better not to say no more about him.

When them old men that hang around the livery barn heard about it they all just laughed theirself sick. Uncle Jack Holmes says, "It ain't no wonder the postmaster is a-feeling bad, but you got to remember that little Jemson was pretty near seventy, and we all got to go sometime." And then all them old loafers got a big wreath off of the undertaker and carried it down to the postoffice. Somebody went in the night and tied fourteen inches of black crape on the doorknob, just like it was a regular funeral. And when the town paper come out on Thursday there was a long poem that started:

> Little Jemson, thou hast left us,
> We shall never see thee more

about how the deceased will be sadly missed all over the country. Nobody knowed who wrote the poem, because it just said "A Friend" at the bottom.

When the postmaster seen that stuff printed right in the paper, he put on his hat and went down to the livery barn. "Listen here, boys," says he, "I ain't blaming nobody, because I started it myself a-talking to that fool schoolmarm, but this thing has went far enough." Uncle Jack Holmes says, "Well, it looks like the drinks are on you, anyhow." So the postmaster

134

TEDDY KETCHUM

ONE TIME there was a fellow named Teddy Ketchum, that kept a-talking about how he didn't get no help from his kinfolks, not even the old woman and the kids. That is the reason Teddy never got no work done, and that's why he was always borrowing stuff from the neighbors, and trying to get credit at the store.

Whenever a stranger come along, Teddy used to tell about

the time he was fighting a panther bare-handed. His wife and the biggest boy just set on a log a-watching the fight. He was getting clawed up something terrible, with most of his clothes tore off, and blood a-running down his legs. Finally he drawed his knife to cut the panther's throat. "Don't stob him, Teddy," says the old woman. "Don't stob the varmint, whatever you do!" Teddy wiped the blood out of his eyes, and he says, "What the hell do you mean, Mary?" The old woman took a fresh chaw of tobacker. "I'm afeared you'll ruin the skin," she says, "and I want it for a bedspread."

The panther slapped the knife out of Teddy's hand just about then, and he couldn't do no more talking for awhile. The varmint got him down, and bit his shoulder all to hell, and was a-trying to scratch his guts out besides. Teddy begun to holler calf-rope, but the folks just set there on the log. Pretty soon the biggest boy says, "It looks like pappy's going to get killed." The old woman studied awhile, and then she says, "I reckon you're right, son." The boy just set there a-watching the fight, but he begun to look kind of uneasy. "Maw," says he, "don't you think I better lend pappy my axe?"

The whole thing was just a made-up tale, of course, but Teddy always told it for the truth. And then he would pull a big butcher knife out of his boot, and begin whetting the edge with a piece of sandrock. Probably the tourists knowed it was a lie, but they never said nothing. Not while Teddy Ketchum set there with that big old butcher knife in his hand.

THE BLOODY MILLER

ONE TIME there was a man named Bland, but he wasn't no relation to Silver Dick. No sir, this fellow lived in Glossip county, and he run a gristmill on the stage coach route. Him and his wife got to fighting, and old man Bland cut her throat. It was hog killing time, so he just ground the corpse up into sausage, and buried the bones under a big flat rock. He put the sausage in cornshucks and smoked it right good. And that's how the old man found out that human sausage is better than pork sausage. The neighbors all said it was the best they ever tasted, but of course they didn't have no idea what kind of meat it was made out of.

About a month after that a young fellow come snooping around the mill, and it was the same one that old man Bland had the trouble with his wife over, so now the young fellow wants to know what become of her. So the old man cut his throat, and ground him into sausage meat too. When he got it seasoned with sage and pepperweed, and smoked right good, the folks all said it was wonderful sausage. But they didn't have no idea what kind of meat it was made out of.

From that time on old man Bland made more sausage than anybody, and he sold lots of it to the stage-coach people. He got a millwright from St. Louis to make him the biggest sausage grinder you ever seen, and it run by water power same as the gristmill. Old man Bland bought all the best pigs for miles around. He bought a lot of venison too, and some veal, and every kind of meat he could get hold of. But he knowed that humans make the best sausage, so he would kill people whenever he got a chance. Two yellow girls from Boonville come along the road, so he just cut their throat and ground them up. And then come a big fat woman to stay all night, and into the grinder she went. Pretty soon the neighbors begun to miss their children every so often, but nobody ever thought that old man Bland had anything to do with it.

Things went on like that for several years, and finally the old man tackled a big lubberly boy from up on Milky River. The boy broke loose and run down the road, a-bleeding like

139

a stuck pig. Old man Bland was right on his heels, waving the big butcher knife. Just then some folks come along in a wagon, and it didn't take long to figure out what become of all them children. It wasn't no time at all till a big crowd got together, and finally somebody found the bones under the big flat rock.

Folks in this country didn't pay much attention to the law in them days, and the sheriff at the county seat never heard about the trouble till it was all over. Him and his deputy come out to the mill and asked a lot of questions, but they didn't find out much. So finally he just added old man Bland's name to the list of people that was missing, and rode back to town.

Some say that the folks throwed the old man into his machine, and ground him up alive. But it ain't likely, because the grinder wasn't big enough for that. Another story is that they just chopped him up with axes, and fed the carcass to the hogs. Probably there ain't anybody alive now that knows just how it happened. But they sure done away with old man Bland somehow, because he never showed up after that night.

The folks had quite a argument about what to do with all the sausage a-hanging in the old man's smokehouse. Nobody wanted to eat the stuff, because maybe it was made out of their own children. But it would be a pity to let so much fine looking sausage go to waste. Finally they just sold it to the stage-coach company, and give the money to a Baptist preacher. There was a man named Pomeroy claimed the church people used it to convert heathen cannibals in the Sandwich Islands, but that was just kind of a joke. That fellow Pomeroy used to work on a newspaper in St. Louis, and everybody knowed better than to believe anything *he* said.

THE SHERIFF GIVE HIM ROPE

ONE TIME there was a fellow named Zack Manners that used to carry the mail. We had a star route up Deer Creek in them days. Everybody liked Zack fine, only about twice a year he would go on a big drunk. And every time he raised so much hell that the folks had to put him in jail. Along in the night, Zack would pound his head on the wall, or tear up the blankets and try to hang himself, so somebody had to set up and watch him. It got to be kind of a nuisance.

Jerdan Baynes was the sheriff then, and he got tired of fooling with Zack Manners. It was about four o'clock when the deputy brought Zack in, a-hollering and cussing so loud you could hear him all over town. Zack kept yelling about how he was going to kill himself. Jerdan listened awhile, and then he went and got a big iron hook. He screwed the hook into a beam right inside the door of Zack's cell. Then Jerdan brought a new rope and tied it on the hook, with a regular hangman's noose in the other end.

"Listen, Zack," says he, "don't tear up no blankets this time. Just use this here rope. All you got to do is climb on the bed, stick your head in the noose, and jump off." And with that the sheriff locked the door and went home. His wife wanted to know who is going to set up with Zack, but Jerdan says, "There ain't nobody going to set up with him, and if the damn fool wants to hang himself he can go right ahead." Him and his wife just laid there in bed, and they could hear Zack a-hollering till about nine o'clock. Everything was quiet after that, but Jerdan didn't get much sleep.

Early next morning Jerdan went over to the jail house, just like he always done. Zack was a-snoring loud as a sawmill, and the rope was still a-hanging on the hook. Pretty soon Zack quit snoring, and Jerdan knowed he had woke up. Jerdan waited awhile, and then he hollered good and loud, "Tell Doc Holton to come over, soon as it's convenient. I want him to examine Zack Manner's corpse, and fill out the papers." Everything was quiet for a minute, and then Zack says, "I ain't dead. I don't need no doctor."

Jerdan walked over and looked through the bars of Zack's cell, like he was terrible surprised. "Why, Zack, you told me you was going to hang yourself!" says he. "I've done made all the arrangements." Zack looked mighty sick, but he was stone sober. "You needn't think I'm going to die, just to please a cold-blooded sheriff," he says. "Take that goddam rope out of my cell." So Jerdan reached between the bars, and twitched the rope off the hook. Along about noon the kinfolks come along, and took Zack home.

That experience with the rope didn't make no teetotaler out of Zack Manners, but it sure slowed him down considerable. He still got drunk once in a while, but nobody ever heard him a-threatening to kill himself after that.

DUNWOODY'S LAST JOKE

ONE TIME there was a fellow named Dunwoody, and he was well fixed. He owned four big farms, and some houses in town, and he had money in the bank besides. But Dunwoody was not a serious minded man. He wouldn't join no church, so he just played around and had a good time.

Dunwoody never did get married till he was pretty near eighty, and then he married a schoolmarm that was only twenty-two years old. The folks all figured the marriage was a mistake, but him and her got along fine. They was always laughing and cracking jokes, anyhow.

Finally the time come for old man Dunwoody to die, and two doctors had give him up. He says to his wife, "Listen, honey, I want you to promise me something." The girl begun to cry, and she says she will do whatever he wants. "It's terrible bad luck," says he, "to break your promise to a dying man." His wife kept hollering that she will never break her word, no matter what happens. So then Dunwoody says very solemn, "Promise me that you will never, never marry a man——" and then his voice choked up like he couldn't talk no more. The young woman looked kind of worried, but she nodded her head just the same. "Never marry a man," says Dunwoody, "if he is more than sixty-five years old."

Dunwoody's wife drawed a deep breath when she heard that, and she says, "Oh, I won't! I promise!" Then she looked the old man right in the eye, and they both busted out laughing. The folks in the next room was plumb scandalized, but him and her just held hands and laughed like fools. Old man Dunwoody was still grinning about it when he died that same evening.

The young widow cried a little then, and she give him a fine big funeral. She always said that Mister Dunwoody was a mighty good husband. But all the rest of her life she had to laugh every time she thought about old Dunwoody's last joke. She didn't have no trouble keeping her promise. It wasn't long till she married a fine healthy fellow about thirty years old, and they lived happy ever after.

143

RIDING ON THE CARS

ONE TIME there was an old woman that lived away back in the mountains. Aunt Hattie was as fine a woman as ever walked, but she hadn't never been very far from home. After the railroad come through, somebody asked her if she ever seen a train. "No, honey," says Aunt Hattie, "but I sure love to hear 'em holler." You could hear the whistle a long way off, over them high ridges.

Finally the kinfolks fixed it up for Aunt Hattie to take a little trip. They drove to town in a spring wagon, and waited around the depot. The boys figured Aunt Hattie might get excited when she seen the engine a-coming, but that old woman wasn't scared of nothing. She just laughed like a little girl. "Law me," she says, "ain't it wonderful how the contraption can blow out smoke?" When the train stopped, Aunt Hattie took her satchel and set down in the coach with the other passengers. You could see the old woman was having a good time, but she never done nothing foolish. Aunt Hattie always acted like a lady, because that's what she was.

When the train got pretty near to Eagle Rock there was a trestle burned out, and they had a bad accident. There was two men killed, and three or four passengers crippled. Aunt Hattie was shook up considerable, but she found her little satchel and got out with the rest of the people. There was a fat drummer running around like a chicken with its head cut off, and he kept a-hollering, "Are you hurt, ma'am? Are you hurt?" Aunt Hattie just looked at him. "No, I ain't hurt," she says, "why do you ask?" The drummer begun to jabber about the wreck, and how terrible it is. "What wreck?" says Aunt Hattie.

The poor drummer was so excited he couldn't hardly talk. But finally he told her how the engine has run off the track, with two men dead and several more hurt pretty bad. So then Aunt Hattie walked up to the front of the train, and seen what had happened. The other passengers kept asking how come Aunt Hattie wasn't scared like the rest of them. "This is the first time I ever rode on the steam cars," she says. "I thought maybe they was accustomed to stop this way."

THE BELLED BUZZARD

ONE TIME there was two boys set a steel trap beside a dead lamb, because maybe they could catch a wolf. If anybody catches a wolf they can take the scalp to the courthouse, and the clerk will give you twenty dollars for a bounty. But when the boys come back next Sunday there was a big old buzzard in the trap, and he was caught by one leg. It is bad luck to kill a buzzard, so they just tied a little bell round his neck and turned the old stinker loose.

About three miles away a young fellow named Tennyson was cutting sprouts. The folks told him not to cut sprouts on Sunday, but he done it anyhow. Well sir, all of a sudden he heard a bell a-ringing, like it was way up in the air. He looked up, and here come a lot of buzzards. They was wheeling around mighty peculiar, with the bell ringing like a fire-engine. Young Tennyson figured it was some kind of a warning, and he was scared plumb witless. Them buzzards swung lower and lower, and the bell kept a-getting louder. Tennyson dropped his grubbing hoe, and took out for the big timber. The further that boy run the worse he felt, and it seemed like the bell was follering right after him. Tennyson had heard them old stories about buzzards a-chasing sinners, and maybe he had something on his conscience.

It was way in the night when Tennyson got home. He was shaking like a leaf, so the folks give him a hot toddy and put him to bed. They told him lots of fellows get sick from working on the Lord's day, but he figured it was something a lot worse than grubbing sprouts. Tennyson was a boy that had never took no interest in church work, but from then on he went to meeting pretty near every night, and twice on Sunday. After they baptised him in the creek, Tennyson went plumb hog wild on religion. He would get up and testify how the Lord sent fowls of the air with bells on 'em, so all of a sudden he seen the light. The folks tried to tell him about the boys that belled the buzzard. But Tennyson says it is a sign out of heaven, and ain't got nothing to do with wolf traps.

Pretty soon he got to running with them jimsonweed Christians up on Pokey Ridge, and the next thing we knowed Tennyson was a full-fledged preacher, holding revival meetings all over the country. Them people meet around in each other's houses, and in brush arbors along the side roads. Tennyson got so he could talk the unknown tongue with the best of 'em, and fetch poison snakes right into the pulpit without getting bit. Sometimes he would go to them holy dances away out in the woods somewheres, and he was always cootering round amongst the womenfolks.

It was a girl named Beulah that finally got Tennyson in trouble, and they give him a year in the county jail. Tennyson didn't have no objections, because he says Jesus was throwed

146

in prison too, and lots of other holy men. There was sixty days off for good behavior, but Tennyson preached to the prisoners every night for ten months, and all the people in the jail was glad when they finally turned him loose.

The home folks never seen much of Tennyson after that, but we all heard about him. Probably he's still a-preaching somewhere out in Oklahoma, or maybe Kansas. Wherever it is, you can bet your boots Tennyson is still telling the people how God sent great flocks of birds with bells on 'em, and that's how he was called to preach the gospel.

A LITTLE PIECE OF THREAD

ONE TIME there was some people lived right near the big highway, and so they was bothered with tramps. Finally the woman put her foot down, and says she is not going to feed no more loafers, because they ought to get a job somewheres. And after that whenever a man ask her for something to eat she would tell him to go away, or else set the dogs on him.

Everything was all right till a young fellow come along, and he was so clean he didn't look like a regular tramp. He says, "Lady, will you please give me a little piece of thread?" She seen the fellow has tore his britches, and he had a needle but no thread. Everybody knows that if a man's clothes ain't mended he can't get no good job in town. So the woman give him a little piece of thread.

The young fellow went down the road and set under a tree for awhile. Then he come back and says, "Lady, I can't fix the pants, because there ain't no cloth for a patch." So the woman give him a little piece of cloth.

About two o'clock the young fellow come to the house again. "Lady," he says, "them pants is so far gone they can't be fixed nohow. It sure would be nice if you would give me a pair of your husband's old pants." The woman grinned when she heard that. "You are a very smart young man," she says. "If you had asked me for the pants at first, I would have set the dogs on you." So then she give him a pair of second-handed britches.

The young fellow went out behind the barn and put the pants on. After while he come back to the house and says, "Lady, these pants is a little big around the waist. But if you was to give me a bite of victuals, I believe they would fit perfect." The woman just busted out laughing, and she says, "You are the smartest young man I have seen in a long time." So then him and her got to talking. Pretty soon it seemed like they was good friends, and the woman give the young fellow a fine big dinner.

It just goes to show that a smart young man can get pretty near anything he wants in this world. But you got to move slow, and be patient, and just take one step at a time.

THE BIG RABBITS

ONE DAY Tip Martin come into town, and he says, "Gentlemen, I have killed the biggest goddam rabbit in the world!" The folks just laughed, but when Tip pulled the critter out of his wagon, they didn't know what to think. That rabbit stood six hands high at the shoulders, with ears eight

148

inches long. It was just a terrible big jackrabbit, of course, but nobody around here had ever seen one before. The whole country was swarming with cottontails in them days, but we didn't have no regular jackrabbits till just a few years back, when they begun to drift in from Kansas and Oklahoma.

The boys hung that rabbit up in front of the butcher shop, and everybody that come along just looked at it, with their eyes sticking out like doorknobs. Next week a fellow says he seen another one over on Kickapoo Barrens, and pretty soon rabbit stories was flying round thick as crows at a hog killing. To hear them boys talk, you'd think them big rabbits was eating us out of house and home. Old man Preston says they have gnawed off fenceposts to get into the corn, and was felling his apple trees just like beavers. Up on Leatherwood Creek they got so big the dogs was afraid to tackle 'em. When a man went to call his hogs the rabbits would come a-running and chase the pigs right out of the lot. They turned over the feeding troughs, and would upset the farmer too, if he didn't get out of the way.

It seemed like them rabbits was getting bigger at every jump, especially the bucks. They could do everything a jack-ass does except bray, and mares all over the country was foaling colts with feet like rabbits. Lots of them was nothing but undersized mules, and no great harm done, but some of the horse colts was fertile. They would just breed around promiscuous with jennies and mares and rabbits and whatever come handy. Pretty soon the whole caboodle was all mixed up, till a fellow didn't know what kind of stock he was raising.

Nobody could tell how much truth there was in them big stories, but any fool could see that things was going from bad to worse. The Lord only knows what would happen next, but all of a sudden them animals took sick, and it was what they call rabbit fever nowadays. Most of the critters died right in the fields, and then come a big snowfall, so the folks went out and killed the rest of 'em off with shotguns. Everything kind of quietened down then, and the grass come green in March the same as always. So that was the end of the rabbit panic.

It all happened a long time ago, and most of the people that remembered the stories are dead now. But everybody knows that Missouri mules are not like other mules. And several of the old-timers still believe that maybe them big rabbits had something to do with it.

HOW TO GET RID
OF DOCTORS

ONE TIME there was a city man come to a little settlement, and he seen a lot of people milling around in the graveyard. So he asked the folks, "What is going on over there?" A country fellow says that Doc Pendergast is dead, and we are giving him a big funeral. Doc was a prominent citizen and well fixed, also he was the best doctor in the whole country.

"Hell," says the city man, "do you bury doctors here?" The country fellow says of course they do, because when a doctor dies he has got to be buried the same as anybody else. The city man just shook his head, like he never heard of such a thing. "They sure have got some peculiar customs in Arkansas," says he.

The country fellow didn't return no answer, but he kept

thinking about it. Next day he seen the city man setting on the porch of the hotel. "Mister," says he, "when a doctor dies back where you come from, what do they do with the body?" The city man says the folks just lay him out in his office and lock the door, but leave the window open. When they unlock the door next morning the doctor is gone, and that's all there is to it. The country fellow was mighty surprised to hear about such a thing. "But what becomes of the corpse?" says he.

The city man looked kind of uneasy. "Nobody knows exactly," he says, "and we don't never talk about it, out of respect for the kinfolks. But there ain't no denying," says he, "that a doctor's office always smells like brimstone in the morning."

THE PREACHER
WOULDN'T EAT

ONE TIME there was a fellow come down here from some big town, and he was a Campbellite preacher. They let him stay at Pap Morgan's place Saturday night, and he was going to have a meeting at the Blue Eye church next morning. The preacher was a pleasant spoken fellow, but he was off his feed, and didn't eat no supper only a piece of huckleberry pie.

The women fixed him a fine breakfast, with a big platter of ham and eggs. "You folks sure do set a good table," says he. "But I don't never eat much breakfast when I'm a-going to preach. Earthly food seems to hinder a true feast of the spirit. My finest sermons has all been preached on a empty stomach." So he just nibbled a little piece of bread, and drunk one cup

151

of coffee. Then the old man hitched up and took him over to the church.

When Pap Morgan got back in the evening he never said nothing about the meeting. So after supper one of the big boys spoke up and says, "Pap, what kind of a sermon did the fellow preach?" The old man grinned a little, and shook his head. "Son," says he, "that there preacher might just as well have et."

THREE FOOT DEEPER

ONE TIME there was a fellow name of Dingle come to Oronogo, only it was called Minersville in them days. The folks around there never done no farming, they just dug up lead to make bullets and counterfeit money. Dingle was a natural born fool, and he couldn't eat no meat or else he would get sick. Somebody ask him if he was a Methodist, and Dingle says, "No, I'm a vegetarian, because I live on corn whiskey and chewing tobacco." There was a hardrock man named Muffet blowed in from Granby and he was just as crazy as Dingle, so they went into partnership.

Them fellows didn't have nothing but a pick and a shovel and a Armstrong hoister, but they staked out a claim anyhow. They dug a hole about ten foot deep that was called the Shaggy Dog mine, but didn't find nothing. When they got down twenty foot the rock was awful hard, and powder cost money, so they sold the Shaggy Dog for two hundred dollars. The fellow that bought it dug about three feet deeper, and struck solid lead ore. So he got rich and lived in a fine painted house. But Dingle and Muffet was just as poor as ever.

152

Pretty soon they went down to Murphytown and got hold of another prospect. This time they sunk a shaft thirty foot deep, and called it Shaggy Dog Number Two. There was a few little chunks of jack, but it didn't amount to nothing. One day a fellow come along and offered to buy them out for three hundred dollars. It was a hot day, and the windlass had broke down, and they had run out of cribbing, so Dingle and Muffet took the money. The fellow that bought Number Two put in a regular whip hoist, with a yoke of oxen to pull up the bucket. He only went about three foot deeper and struck solid lead ore. So he got rich and went into the saloon business. But Dingle and Muffet was still broke.

Soon as they drunk up the three hundred dollars, the boys started out to hunt a grubstake. They was both pretty mad by this time. "It looks like you and me do the work," says Muffet, "but them high-collared roosters gets all the gravy." Dingle just took another chaw of tobacco. "It's this here selling out that ruined us," says he. "From now on we won't sell out no more, till after we go three foot deeper." Muffet thought about it awhile, and scratched his head. "There's something wrong with your reasoning, but I can't just put my finger on it," says he. "I figure we better go *six* foot deeper, just to be on the safe side."

The folks was always telling stories about Dingle and Muffet, so the Shaggy Dog prospectors got to be kind of a joke all over the district. Muffet struck it rich later on, and was one of the biggest operators in the whole country. But poor Dingle went out West somewhere, and nobody ever did find out what become of him.

THE NECESSITIES OF LIFE

ONE TIME there was some fellows went deer hunting, and they come to a piece of mighty rough country. It was all steep hills and big rocks, with lots of underbrush besides. There wasn't no road for miles, and no timber cut, so you wouldn't think anybody lived there. But all of a sudden they come to a little shanty, with a old man setting out in front.

The hunters stopped to pass the time of day with the old fellow. He says "Howdy" polite enough, but they couldn't get nothing out of him. Whatever one of the boys would talk about, the old man says he never heard tell of it. He never seen a newspaper for years at a time, and didn't take no interest in politics. He didn't even know how the election turned out, or the war, or even the World Series. They could see he wasn't no hunter, and he didn't give a damn about farming, and he was too old a man to cut wood for a living.

There wasn't no cow in sight, nor no chickens, nor no crops, not even a garden patch. The boys couldn't figure out how the old fellow kept himself in victuals. Finally one of them says, "Living away out here, ain't it hard to get the necessities of life?" The old man understood that question, all right. "It sure is, stranger," says he. "And half the time, when you do get it, the damn stuff ain't fit to drink!"

RIDDLE ME THIS

ONE TIME some fellows in the tavern got to telling riddles. And Jim Blansett says, "Well, there was a donkey tied to a rope, and the rope was only eight feet long, but the carrots was thirty yards away. How did the donkey get to the carrots?" They all thought about it awhile. "I guess you want me to give up," says young Billy Ross, "so then you can say 'that's what the other jackass done.'" But Jim says, "No, that ain't it. The jackass eat the carrots all right. But how did he do it?"

Them boys all scratched their head awhile, and had another drink, but they couldn't figure out how the donkey got the carrots if the rope was only eight foot long. So finally young Billy Ross says, "It can't be done nohow, and so I give up." Jim Blansett just laughed right in everybody's face, and he says, "I see you fellows don't know much about riddles." So then Billy bought another drink, and he says, "Well, let's have the answer, as I want to know how the jackass got to the carrots."

Jim Blansett laughed some more, and then he says the donkey just walked over to the carrots and eat all he wanted. "What about the rope that is only eight foot long?" says Billy. "He just dragged the rope behind him, because the other end of the rope wasn't tied to anything," says Jim Blansett. And then he laughed louder than ever, and he says any jackass is smarter than a lot of people he knows. Young Billy Ross seen how he has been took in, but he says, "Hell, that ain't no riddle, that is just goddam foolishness, because nobody would

155

put a rope on a jackass without they tied the other end to a post."

One word led to another, and pretty soon Billy Ross and Jim Blansett was fighting like wildcats. And then some other fellows begun to join in, so it wasn't no time till they busted up pretty near everything in the place, and the fellow that run the tavern sent after the town marshal. Two or three boys was cut bad, and it is God's own luck they didn't kill somebody. Several of them fellows was mad for a long time after that, and Poody Henders never did get over having a piece chawed out of his ear. It all seems kind of silly now, but riddles was took plumb serious in them days.

THE MAN FROM TEXAS

ONE TIME there was a fellow that lived in Arkansas, but he was born and raised in Texas. So most of the time he just set around bragging about the Lone Star State, and he says Texas is just the same as Paradise. The home folks didn't think much of this kind of talk, because it looked like he was running down Arkansas. Texas is all right, maybe, but anybody that has been there knows it ain't no heaven on earth.

Pretty soon a man from Yellville begun to tell a story about a Texan that died, and he was trying to get into Heaven. Saint Peter talked with him awhile, but the Texan didn't do nothing but jingle his big spurs and brag up Texas. Finally Saint Peter opened the gate, and he says, "Well, you can come in. But I'm afraid you won't like it here." The Arkansawyers all laughed at that story, but the man from Texas says he don't see nothing funny about it.

So then a man from Hot Springs begun to tell a story about another Texan that died, and when he got to the pearly gate they ask where did he come from? "I was borned and raised in Texas," says he. The angel opened up the gate. "Come right in, brother," says the angel, "you have been in Hell long enough!" The Arkansawyers all laughed at that story, but the man from Texas says he don't see nothing funny about it.

Next a fellow from Bald Knob told a story about another Texan that died, and when he come to the big gate it was wide open, so he could see what was going on inside. The Texan stood there a-fanning himself with his big hat, and he says, "Gosh, I didn't know Heaven was so much like Texas." The gatekeeper just looked at him kind of sorrowful. "Son," he says, "this ain't Heaven." The Arkansawyers all laughed at that story, but the man from Texas says he don't see nothing funny about it.

Them fellows from Texas can read and write, fiddle and fight, knock up and throw down. They can holler loud, shoot straight, and jump high. But it seems like most of 'em is kind of dumb, when it comes to appreciating a funny story.

A BARREL OF POPCORN

ONE TIME there was two brothers named Craig that run a little store at the crossroads. They had the best stock of general merchandise in the neighborhood, with meat and groceries and canned goods and hardware and harness and lots of other stuff. "If you don't see what you

157

want, ask for it," says one of the Craig brothers. "If we ain't got it, we'll get it," says the other one. They was both good fellows, and everybody liked them. But they took the store mighty serious, and it was kind of comical sometimes.

Old Jim Pickard hung around the crossroads a good deal, and he was always playing tricks on the Craig boys because they was so goddam solemn about everything. One time he come in and says, "Give me fifty cents worth of popcorn." The Craig brothers didn't have none, because there ain't no demand for it, as the people around here don't give a damn for popcorn. Jim kind of grumbled when they told him that, and he says it's mighty funny a man has to go somewheres else whenever he wants a little poke of something to eat.

Next day Jim got a pocket full of nickels, and he begun sending children down to Craig's store to buy popcorn. He got quite a few grown people to go along, after he told 'em it was a joke on the Craig brothers. About the third day the store was full of people a-hollering for popcorn. "It's a regular goddam fad," says one of the Craig boys, "the folks in this town has went crazy about popcorn all of a sudden." So finally they sent to Joplin and got a whole barrel of the stuff.

After that when anybody come in the store the Craigs would say, "Well, we got that popcorn for you." And the customers would answer, "I sure had a hankering for popcorn last week, but I'm plumb out of the notion now." Or else maybe he would say, "Me and my wife drove to town the other day, and bought enough popcorn to last us six months." So the Craig brothers just set there, and looked at that barrel of popcorn.

Old Jim Pickard come in pretty near every day after that, and he always grinned when he seen the barrel. Once in a while he would buy a nickel's worth. "It sure is fine," says he,

158

"to have a place right handy where a man can get popcorn when he wants it." Jim Pickard was the only man who ever bought any, and the Craig brothers was stuck with it. They knowed there was something fishy about the popcorn craze, but neither one of 'em said much. Maybe they never did figure out that it was just one of Jim Pickard's jokes.

CHANGE THE NAME
OF ARKANSAS?

ONE TIME there was a fellow got himself elected to the legislature at Little Rock. Some say he was a Yankee that sneaked in by mistake, but maybe he was just crazy, or else somebody put him up to it. Anyhow, he kept saying that the name of the Bear State is spelled with an *s* on the end of it, so why don't we pronounce it to rhyme with Kansas? The folks thought he was just fooling at first, but finally he got up and introduced a bill to make it legal. In one minute every man was on his feet, hollering loud as they could. The Speaker was pounding like a blacksmith, and lawmakers was a-cussing all over the place. There was several men tried to make speeches, but the folks didn't pay no attention. Most of them was so mad they couldn't talk, anyhow. But one old gentleman had a voice like a steamboat whistle. "Mister Speaker! Mister Speaker!" he yelled, and the girls could hear him clear up to the Capital Hotel. And so things finally got quiet enough to hear what the old gentleman had to say.

"Mister Speaker, these are times that try men's souls, and every time I try to get the floor you wiggle around like a dog with a flee in his rectum! Change the name of Arkansas? Great

159

God Almighty damn! I'm Senator Cassius M. Johnson from Johnson county, gentlemen. I was born in a log cabin, rocked in a gum cradle, cut my teeth on a six-shooter, and killed three Republicans before I was seven years old. Suckled by a wolf with four rows of tits, and holes punched for more! I got steel hoofs, cast-iron kidneys, and fourteen ribs to a side. Change the name of Arkansas? Hell's fire, no! I can slide down a honey-locust backwards with a wildcat in each hand, and never get a goddam scratch. Blood's my natural drink, and the groans of the dying is music to my ears. Stand back and give me room! Let each man pile his dead according to his taste. You might massacre me, gentlemen, but you can't change the name of the State of Arkansas!

"Down in Johnson county, gentlemen, men are still men and women are glad of it. Change the name of Arkansas? Great God Almighty damn! At fourteen years of age I was swinging a corncob thirteen inches long, the pride and joy of the whole settlement. Change the name of Arkansas? Not while I can stand! My pants was made of rawhide with hair on, and I could fling water half way across the Ouachita!"

Some people began to holler "Out of order! Out of order!" and the Speaker was a-hollering too, but Senator Johnson went right ahead.

"Of course it was out of order," says he, "or else I'd have throwed water clear across the river! What the hell are these people talking about? Change the name of Arkansas? Hell and damnation, no! Would you liken the fair state of Arkansas to that miserable patch of gopher dung that Yankees call Kansas? Would you compare the light of the noonday sun in all its glory to the feeble glimmer of a lightning-bug's hind end? You can holler till the cows come home with bulls on their backs, and then rub your nose in it. But you can't change the name of Arkansas!

"You may foul the most hallowed sanctums of this great republic, gentlemen. You may empty your stinking entrails on Thomas Jefferson's grave, and use the Constitution of the United States for bumfodder. But change the name of Arkansas? Great God Almighty damn! You may rape the Goddess of Liberty in broad daylight, and wipe your unholy member with the Declaration of Independence. But you can't change the name of Arkansas! Tear the stars out of heaven, if you feel like doing something. Soak the sky in a chamber-pot! Loosen the belly-band of Time, and turn the sun and moon out to pasture! But change the name of Arkansas? Hell's fire, no! Not while a single patriot lives to prevent such desecration!"

The story don't say just what happened after Senator Johnson finished his great speech. There was a lot of whooping and hollering, of course, and people running up to shake hands with him. That night he give the speech again down at the hotel, so the boys in the back room could hear it. From then on the old gentleman just kind of visited around the saloons and whorehouses where somebody would buy the drinks, and they always wanted to hear him tell how he saved the name of Arkansas. There was several other boys that used to give the speech too, especially Charley Osborne that put on false whiskers so he looked just like Senator Johnson. Also a fellow at the Elks Club was pretty good at it, and then regular play-actors was doing the same thing all over the country.

After while the whole thing got to be kind of a joke. Lots of the people that heard the speech thought it was just something them saloon men had made up. They did not believe a Senator ever said anything like that in the legislature. But

161

the home folks didn't see nothing unreasonable about it. They knowed that the best speeches in the world is made by politicians. And any Senator in Arkansas can make just as good a speech as them trout-mouthed congressmen they got up North.

JOHNNY'S LITTLE DOG

ONE TIME there was a boy named Johnny and he had a little dog. It was one of these curly-haired dogs that could swim like a duck, and when anybody throwed a stick he would fetch it right back to you. Johnny used to tie a rock on the stick so it would sink, but that didn't make no difference. If you throwed one of them weighted sticks in the river, the dog would swim right out and dive for it. Johnny's little dog was awful good at that, and he would fetch the stick right back to whoever throwed it.

Johnny's folks all thought a lot of that dog, until the time some of the menfolks went a-fishing. The water was too murky for gigging, and the fish wouldn't bite on hooks, so the folks put all their bait in a deep hole, to draw the fish so they could kill 'em with dynamite. When the stuff goes off, the fish all come a-floating up to the top. Everybody used to fish that way, but it's against the law now. Johnny's old daddy put the cap on a stick of dynamite, with a good long fuse. And then he lit the fuse, and throwed it away out in the deep water.

Nobody ever thought about the little dog, but he just swum out and got the dynamite, because he thought it was a stick for him to fetch. And here he come with the stuff in his mouth, and the fuse a-sputtering. The men all hollered and throwed

162

rocks, but the little dog just kept a-coming. Everybody run fast as they could. Johnny's daddy took right out through the woods, but it looked like the dog was a-gaining on him. Just as the dog was about to catch him, the old man jumped off a bluff about twenty foot high, and lit in some cedar trees. Then come a big BOO-OO-OOM, that scattered rocks and dirt all over everything. Johnny's daddy was shook up and bruised and scratched something terrible, but there wasn't no bones broke.

The boys got the old man back down to the river, and washed the blood and dirt off him. They put whiskey on the scratches, and give him several big drinks to steady his nerves. So pretty soon he got to feeling better, but he was still pretty shaky, and he says it is the awfullest experience he ever went through.

They built a good fire and set around awhile. Everybody took a few more snorts out of the jug. And then some of the boys went back to look for Johnny's little dog, but they never did find hide nor hair of him.

THERE'S A SLEIGHT TO IT

ONE TIME there was a farmer named Rube Stockstill, and he had to have a operation. It was a little operation that didn't amount to much, and Doc Holton done it in fifteen minutes. So then he says, "Doc, how much do I owe you?" But when Doc told him forty dollars Rube hollered like a stuck pig, because forty dollars was a lot of money in them days.

"Listen, Rube," says the doctor, "this operation ain't so easy as you think, because there is a sleight to it." But Stockstill says forty dollars is too much for fifteen minutes work, no matter if there's a sleight to it or not. "It's true that the operation only took a few minutes," Doc says, "but I spent many years, and thousands of dollars, learning how to do these operations." Rube Stockstill kept on a-hollering, so Doc says, "Hell, you needn't pay me any cash. You can just cut me some wood this winter." Rube finally says all right, but he wasn't satisfied by no means.

Along that fall Rube brought in eight loads of wood, and ricked it up beside Doc Holton's house. "There she is, Doc," says he, "and I'm sure glad we're all square." Doc begun to holler murder and rape. "Hell's fire, Rube," he says, "I can get wood anywhere for seventy-five cents! What do you mean, charging me five dollars a rick?" Old Stockstill just grinned. "Chopping wood ain't so easy as you might think, Doc," says he. "There's a sleight to it. Why, I spent forty years a-learning how to cut wood like that."

Doc seen that Rube had him where the hair's short, so he didn't say no more. But it was the last time that them two ever swapped work. The whole Stockstill tribe has to pay cash nowadays, even if they don't want nothing but a nickel's worth of itch-medicine.

ON TRIAL FOR HIS LIFE

ONE TIME there was a fellow come to our town, and some say he had been raised in Kansas. The folks didn't like him much, but they treated him the best they could, so long as he behaved himself. But pretty soon he got to bragging a good deal, and then he took up abusing the citizens. It got so that whenever he come into a saloon, the decent people would finish their drink and then they would go out. So finally the men that run the groceries told him they didn't want his business. After that he acted meaner than ever, and the home folks was getting pretty tired of being pushed around by a goddam Yankee anyhow.

One day he says something insulting to a little man from up on Bull Creek. He was a ragged old fellow with whiskers, that was just tending to his own business and not bothering nobody. The little man says, "You are too big for me to fight, and I ain't got the difference with me." The big Yankee just laughed contemptuous, and he says, "Go get your gun, and I will show you how we do things up where I come from." So the little man went down to the wagon yard and got his rifle. It was an old Sharps buffalo gun, that took a brass shell big as a corncob, and the bullets run about twelve to the pound.

When the Yankee seen the little man a-coming, he pulled out his six-shooter and let it off three times, but he didn't hit nothing. The little man just fired the old Sharps once, but it knocked the Yankee clear out in the street, and killed him dead as a doornail. You could see smoke a-drifting around for ten minutes afterward, and big paper wads a-smoldering on the sidewalk. "It was a fair fight, gentlemen," says the little fellow. "I never killed a man in my life, without he had a weapon in his hand." And everybody that seen the killing knowed it was the truth.

In them days the folks never messed with a case like that, but there was several johnny-come-lately lawyers at the county seat, and they set up a great holler about it. So the prosecuting attorney was forced to have a regular trial in court, though everybody knowed in reason that the jury was bound to turn the little man loose. Old Barney Finn had saw the whole thing, so they made him tell all about it. "How far were you from the deceased, when he was shot down by this here defendant?" one of them smart-aleck lawyers asked him. "Three yards, two feet, and seven inches," says Barney Finn.

The town lawyer was considerable set back when he heard that. "A very unusual answer, Mister Finn," says he. "Tell the jury how come you know the distance so exact." Barney looked at the judge. "Do I have to tell 'em?" says he. The judge says yes, and for him to remember he is under oath. "Well," says Barney, "I just thought some goddam pettifogger would ask me that, so I measured it."

All the folks in the courtroom laughed like hell, and the fellows on the jury laughed louder than anybody. Even the judge had to grin, and the smart-aleck lawyer didn't ask no more questions. The trial didn't amount to much after that. Everybody knowed how things was, anyhow. So the jury just turned the little man with the whiskers loose, and that's all there was to it.

WOLVES ARE MY BROTHERS

ONE TIME there was a girl named Jenny, and she married a fellow that was part Indian. They lived away back in the woods, as he says the wolves are my brothers, and we don't need no neighbors. Her friends thought Jenny had led her ducks to a poor puddle, because that Indian was wild as a mink. So finally Jenny made up her mind to run off, and go back to her folks. Soon as the fellow went a-hunting, she put on her best clothes and started for the settlement.

She walked through the woods a ways, and here come a big wolf. The wolf was going to eat Jenny up, but she throwed down her bonnet. So the wolf picked up the bonnet and away he run.

She just walked on through the woods, and here come another big wolf. The wolf was going to eat Jenny up, but she

throwed down her coat. So the wolf picked up the coat and away he run.

Jenny just kept a-walking, and here come another big wolf. The wolf was going to eat Jenny up, but she pulled off her dress and throwed it down. So the wolf picked up the dress and away he run.

167

She was feeling mighty funny, but Jenny walked right on anyhow. When the next wolf come along she throwed down her petticoat. So the wolf picked up the petticoat and away he run.

Poor Jenny was considerable slowed down now, but here come another wolf, and she had to pull off her drawers. It wasn't no time at all till the next wolf showed up, and took her undershirt.

So there was Jenny a-standing out in the woods, without a stitch on but her moccasins. "I sure can't go into town like this," she says, "and it's too cold for me to be walking around naked as a jaybird, anyhow." So then she started back toward her old man's house. Jenny was worried about what might happen, when he seen her clothes was gone. "If I tell him about them wolves, he'll think it is a lie," she says to herself.

Pretty soon here come a big wolf with the undershirt, and he throwed it down. So Jenny put on the undershirt and walked towards home. And here come another wolf with the drawers, and he throwed them down. So Jenny put on the drawers and walked towards home. Then here come another big wolf with the petticoat, and soon as Jenny put the petticoat on she began to feel better. Pretty soon another wolf brought her dress, and another wolf brought her coat, and finally here come the last big wolf a-carrying the bonnet.

When she got back to the cabin Jenny was all dressed, and the old man didn't say a word. He just looked at her, and grinned kind of wolfish. And she says to herself, "Maybe them wolves are his brothers, sure enough." So after that Jenny didn't run off no more, but stayed home and took care of the house, like she ought to have done in the first place. The folks

168

all say that him and her raised a fine family, and lived happy
ever after.

OLD HORNY

ONE TIME there was some boys going
to drown a litter of hound pups, and just then a man come
along. He lived away up the river under a bluff, like a regular
hermit. Some folks thought he was hiding out from the law,
but maybe he was just one of them fellows that likes to live
by himself. Anyhow, he says he needed a dog the worst way,
so the boys give him one of the hound pups. He took it home
to his camp under the bluff. The pup growed mighty fast, because he fed it on goat's milk.

The hermit didn't have no neighbors, so the pup was raised
in the wilderness. He knowed all about foxes and coons and
bobcats, but never had nothing to do with dogs. The reason
he didn't learn how to bark, was because he never heard no
other dogs bark. That pup had the damndest voice you ever
heard. He was what foxhunters call a bugle-mouth, only louder
and terrible high. When he give tongue on a still night, it
sounded like a silver trumpet blowing away off in hell. Some
folks thought the Devil must be mixed up with it, and that's
why they called the hound Old Horny.

When the home folks heard Old Horny a-bawling they just
shivered, and let on like it wasn't nothing out of the ordinary.
But if a stranger heard it he was scared goddam near to death,
and some of 'em just went plumb crazy. Sometimes women
would holler and tear their clothes, or maybe lay down in the

dusty road. A preacher from Kansas City run right through the creek, and never even knowed he was up to his elbows in ice-cold water. The boys generally told the tourists it was a panther on the warpath. It was just a waste of breath to tell 'em the truth, because they wouldn't believe no dog could make a noise like that.

The hermit run around with Old Horny all the time, and pretty soon folks begun to talk about how he was acting mighty peculiar. Some say that him and Old Horny got to trailing strangers through the hills, and treed women just like you would a coon. Finally the folks found a girl dead over on Granny Branch, and it wasn't no common murder. Some of the boys went to the hermit's place that night, and nobody knows what they found. But it must have been something pretty bad, because they killed the hermit right there, and shot Old Horny, too. Three months later some tourists found the hermit's corpse in the river, so far gone that the sheriff just burned it on a pile of driftwood. Nobody ever did find the dead dog, though.

Some of the old timers say that Old Horny wasn't really dead, and there's folks on Granny Branch that claim they still hear him sometimes, a-bawling along the high ridges of a night. But maybe it ain't so. You know how stories get started about things like that. And the people that live on Granny Branch are mostly damn fools, anyhow.

SHE WANTED A DIVORCE

ONE TIME a woman was trying to get a divorce, because she claimed her husband ain't no good. But the fellow was a-standing right there in the courtroom, and he says it is a outrageous lie. So the judge says, "Well, how long have you two been married?" and the woman says three years. "How many children have you got?" says the judge, and they showed him the three children.

The judge thought about it awhile. "There ain't no way to divide up three children," says he. "Why don't you live together another year? Then you'll have four kids, and you can take two a-piece."

The woman just stood there with her mouth open, but the man spoke up. "That's worse and more of it, judge," says he. "If I top her again, she's liable to have twins."

"Twins!" hollered the woman. "He's just a-bragging, judge. Why, if I'd depended on *him,* we wouldn't even have these three we got!"

The poor husband didn't have no answer to that one, and neither did the judge. So they just give the woman her divorce, and called it a day.

BACKHOUSE ALBERT'S MONEY

ONE TIME there was an old man that done odd jobs for the people around town. The boys used to call him Backhouse Albert, because he would clean out a privy for two dollars, so naturally he didn't smell like no lady's

perfume. Albert wore old clothes that folks give him for nothing, and he never spent a nickel. The poor old fellow didn't own no land, but just squatted on a patch of ground that belonged to the railroad. That way he didn't have to pay no rent, or taxes neither. The folks used to say that Backhouse

Albert must have money buried somewhere, but it was just kind of a joke.

Finally the old man's shanty caught fire in the night, while he was asleep. Probably it started from a little tin stove, that somebody had throwed away. Anyhow, here come Albert with his clothes afire, and he rolled in the snow to put himself out. He wasn't hurt much, but the shanty burnt plumb to the ground. Everything in the place was gone, and it's lucky Albert always slept in his clothes, or he wouldn't have nothing left. Doc Holton bandaged him up free, and the sheriff let him sleep in the jail till morning.

It was about noon when Albert come down to the bank, and he says, "I want to put some money in your big safe." The fellow that run the bank just laughed, and he says all right. The old man had a money belt round his middle, and he counted out ten thousand dollars. There was lots of business men in town that didn't have that much, and the banker was plumb flabbergasted. Albert had more money left in the belt, too. He says he is going over to Durgenville and put the rest of it in the other bank, because a man would be a fool to trust all his eggs in one basket. Albert was going to walk the twelve miles through the snow, but the boys give him a ride, because they was afraid something might happen to the old fellow.

All the loafers around town was mighty polite to Albert, after they found out he was rich. And there was a man come all the way from Kansas City to write a story about him, so they could print it in the paper. Everybody wanted to know how Backhouse Albert got all that money. "I done it by working hard, and never spending a cent," says Albert. The fellow from Kansas City asked Albert if he had ever been robbed. "Just one time, and it sure learned me a lesson," Albert says. The newspaper fellow kept a-pestering him to find out just how it happened.

"Well," says Albert, "back in 1898 a man give me two drinks of applejack, and the stuff went to my head." The fellow from Kansas City says "What did you do then?" Albert didn't want to talk about such a terrible experience, but finally he says, "Well, I got kind of bewildered, and whooped off considerable money." The fellow just kept on asking questions. "Well," says Backhouse Albert, "I let a storekeeper talk me into paying twenty-five cents for a pair of socks!"

THE CAT'S FOOT

ONE TIME there was a fellow over in the Territory, and he was losing meat. That was a terrible bad thing, because country folks was honest in them days, and nobody ever thought of locking their smokehouse door. If somebody run out of meat he just come to his neighbor like a man and borrowed a couple of hams or a side of bacon, and paid it back when he could. Things is different nowadays, of course.

Well sir, this fellow which his meat was gone didn't say nothing, but he went and hid in the smokehouse. Pretty soon a great big cat walked in. It was pretty near big as a panther. The fellow drawed his bowie knife, twelve inches long and sharp as a razor. When the big cat pulled down a ham the fellow made a lunge, and cut one of its feet right off. Then he run for the house, and got in bed. The big old cat was a-tearing around ouside, a-screaming fit to wake the dead. Finally it quietened down, but the folks didn't get much sleep that night.

Next morning a peckerwood come a-riding in to get the doctor. He says his wife was fooling with the axe, and cut her foot off accidental. The woman bled to death, in spite of all Doc could do. They do say she died a-yowling and a-spitting like a cat. Some of the neighbors told it around that they found a woman's foot in the smokehouse. Maybe they did, and then again it might be they didn't. But the fellow never lost no more meat, anyhow.

LITTLE TOODY

ONE TIME there was a man working in his strawberries, and he found the prettiest little rock you ever seen. His old woman says such things is all foolishness, but he took the rock home anyhow, and set it on the fireboard. Everybody knows a rock with a hole in it is good luck, and we could sure use some good luck in this family, says he.

Next day the old woman went along to work in the strawberries, too. And when they got home that night, the house was all cleaned up. There was cookwood split, and fresh water in the bucket, and the dishes all washed besides. The woman says it is mighty funny how somebody come in and done all that, but the man he just laughed. "Little Toody is a awful good hand around the house," says he. And when the old woman wanted to know who is Little Toody, he just pointed to the rock with the hole in it that was setting on the fireboard.

After that the house was all cleaned up while the man and his wife was out, and some days the victuals was cooked, too. The man says he thinks Little Toody is a better cook than the old woman. Every night the woman would look at the rock with the hole in it, but she couldn't see nothing out of the ordinary. Then one evening the man got home first, and when the woman come in there was a pretty girl setting beside him. So she says to the girl, "Who are you?" And the girl says, "They call me Little Toody." The woman looked up at the fireboard, and the rock with the hole in it was gone.

The old man was away from home a good deal that summer, and it seemed like he had to go somewhere pretty near every day. Whenever he was away, the rock with the hole in it was gone, too. Finally the old woman woke up one night, and she seen him and the girl in the moonlight down by the barn. They wasn't playing tit-tat-toe, neither. So she looked to see if the rock with the hole in it was setting on the fireboard, but the rock was gone. The old woman was pretty mad, but she just let on like she hadn't woke up. Next morning the man went out to milk, and the woman seen the pretty little rock was back on the fireboard. So all of a sudden she grabbed the rock and throwed it down the deep well.

Her and the man worked in the strawberries all day. When they got home that night the house was not cleaned up, and there wasn't no cookwood split, and the water bucket was empty. The man seen that the rock with the hole in it was gone. "It looks like our good luck has left us," says he. The old woman didn't return no answer. The man looked all over the place for the rock with the hole in it, but Little Toody was gone for good. So the old woman had to do her own housework from then on. Lots of times she wished Little Toody was back, but there ain't no way to get rocks out of a drilled well. And so that is the end of the story.

ADAM AND EVE

ONE TIME there was a preacher that couldn't read, but he knowed most of the Book by heart, and preached better than lots of these here educated parsons. Sometimes he would tell funny stories about people in the Old Testament. Them stories ain't in the Bible at all, so maybe he just made 'em up as he went along.

Like the time he was telling about what Adam and Eve done after they was throwed out of Eden. It seemed like they lived in a little town, and every morning they walked out to the farm where they was cutting sprouts for some foreigner. It was a long way and a rough road, and the whole family was barefooted. One evening they was dragging their ass home all tired out, and they come past a fine plantation, with a white house and a good spring right by the road. There was a big apple orchard, and a red barn, and bluegrass in the front yard, and nice flowerbeds on both sides of the porch.

One of the little boys looked in between the palings, and seen how everything was. "Mammy," says he, "wouldn't it be fine if we lived in a place like that?" Eve didn't return no answer, but Adam says, "Son, me and maw used to live in that very place, before you was borned." The kids was all surprised to hear it. "Pappy," says one of the girls, "how come we ain't there now?" Adam grinned. "Well," says he, "the facts of the matter is, your mammy just eat us out of house and home!" Eve looked at Adam out of the corner of her eye, and then they both busted out laughing.

Some high-collared people in town thought it was wrong for

a preacher to tell stories like that, but us home folks don't see no harm in it. We knowed that if God Almighty didn't like them sermons he could put a stop to it easy enough. And so long as the Lord God figured that our preacher was doing all right, who cares what them educated son-of-a-bitches think about it?

NOTES

IN THE following notes, "Motif" and "Type" refer to *Motif-Index of Folk-Literature* by Stith Thompson and *The Types of the Folk-Tale* by Antti Aarne and Stith Thompson. These two books contain keys to published European folklore collections, as well as to the indices of folk tales in the European folklore archives.

THE TALKING TURTLE

Told by Mr. George E. Hastings, Fayetteville, Ark., January, 1942. He got it from a student at the University of Arkansas. Cf. the "Talking Turtle" story reported by Allsopp, *Folklore of Romantic Arkansas,* 1931, II, 189–90; and W. A. Percy, *Lanterns on the Levee,* 1941, pp. 294–96. I published this item as "A Folktale from Arkansas" in the *Tennessee Folklore Society Bulletin* (XIX, 4 [December, 1953], pp. 102–3). (V.R.)

Reports of this story from English-speaking white informants are rare. The story is usually told by Negroes, and I believe it is of African origin. Nearly all versions retain the admonition that too much talk brings one to trouble. Negro texts with a talking turtle, terrapin, or cooter, have been reported by Parsons (*Journal of American Folklore,* XXX, 177, second version) from North Carolina; Fauset (*Journal of American Folklore,* XL, 263) from Alabama; B. A. Botkin (*Lay My Burden Down,* Chicago, 1945, p. 7) from an Oklahoma informant who had been a slave in Texas. Botkin (*Treasury of Southern Folklore,* p. 510) reprints the Mississippi text given by W. A. Percy (see above). Brewer (*Publications of the Texas Folklore Society,* X, 48–50) give a Texas version with a talking bullfrog. In a footnote to Brewer's story, J. Frank Dobie gives a text in which a turtle plays a banjo and sings over and over, "Live in peace; don't tell all you see." This is surprisingly like the African version from the Gold Coast Colony given in adapted form by H. Courlander and G. Herzog (*The Cow-Tail Switch,* New York, 1947, pp. 65–71), which also has a singing and playing tortoise.

In the original form of this Gold Coast story the man is put to death when the tortoise refuses to perform publicly. This grim outcome to talking too much is also found in a closely related story, told in both Africa and America. In the Nupe version given by L. Frobenius and D. C. Fox (*African Genesis,* New York, 1937, pp. 161–62), a hunter finds a human skull and asks, "What brought you here?" The skull replies, "Talking brought me here." The hunter reports the talking skull to the king, who sends guards with him to kill the hunter if he can't prove his statement. When the skull remains obdurately silent, the hunter is killed. After the guard has left, the skull ironically asks the dead hunter's head the hunter's original question, "What brought you here?" The head replies, "Talking brought me here."

American Negro versions of this talking skull story have been published by Parsons (*Journal of American Folklore,* XXX, 176–77) from North Carolina; Fauset (*Journal of American Folklore,* XLI, 536–37) from Pennsylvania; and by Z. N. Hurston (*Mules and Men,* Philadelphia, 1935, pp. 219–20) from Florida. Dorson (*Western Folklore,* XIII, 256–58) gives a lengthy version from a Michigan Negro informant in which a rather verbose mule warns the Negro he talks too much. When he reports to his Boss that the mule talks, the Boss threatens to hang him just to scare him. Later the Negro overhears the Boss say the Negro is crazy and will have to be shot. The text is an odd combination of the talking turtle story with the popular humorous tale "All Things Talk." (H.H.)

BLOOD IN THE CELLAR

Told by Mrs. Rose Spaulding, Eureka Springs, Ark., November, 1951. She had it from a woman who lived near Cassville, Mo. Cf. *Fantasy & Science Fiction,* November, 1953, p. 89. (V.R.)

This is apparently an old tale that has been given a modern

180

sophisticated twist. I assume that the older story was a scary one in which a supernatural figure warned a girl not to speak of him. When she is disobedient, he either takes her away or kills her. For good examples of this pattern see the abstracts given by Parsons, *Antilles,* III, pp. 133–34, No. 139. Some variation of Motif T 541.1.1, "Birth from blood-clot," fits this story, but none of the references given under that Motif apply here. (H.H.)

THE CURSE OF MONEGAW

Told by Mr. William Hatton, Columbia, Mo., July, 1929. He got the storty in St. Clair county, Mo., about 1907. Cf. the account of Monegaw in Jean Graham's *Tales of the Osage River Country,* Clinton, Mo., 1929, pp. 23–28, also *Western Folklore,* XIV, 1 (January, 1955), pp. 24–25. (V.R.)

THE FOREIGNER'S HEAD

Told by Mr. Frank Payne, Galena, Mo., November, 1932. It was an old story in Taney county, Mo., in 1910. This business of cutting off heads is common in backwoods tales of the supernatural. See the *Bulletin of the Missouri Historical Society* (VI [July, 1950], 486–87) for a related item from Howard county, Mo. Cf. *Western Folklore,* XIV, 1 (January, 1955), pp. 23–24. (V.R.)

The cut-off head that talks is well known in folktales. See Motif D 1610.5, "Speaking head." H. Bett (*English Legends,* London, 1952, p. 48) and C. Hole (*English Folklore,* 2d ed., revised, London, 1945, p. 145) tell about St. Edmund's head, which could not be found until it called out, "Here, here, here!" But Mr. Randolph's tale, with its suggestion that the whole business was an illusion caused by hypnotism, belongs under Motif E 783.1, "Head cut off and successfully replaced," and is clearly allied with trickster-magician stories, such as those found in the third part of the chapbook of Dr. Faustus. See P. M. Palmer and R. P. More (*Sources of the Faust Tradition,* New York, 1936, pp. 213–14). This reprints chapter 47 of the 1592 London edition of *The Historie of the Damnable Life, and Deserved Death of Doctor John Faustus.* I have variants of the story in my forthcoming New Jersey collection. (H.H.)

Told by Mr. Elbert Short, Crane, Mo., June, 1933. He had it from neighbors at Marionville, Mo. The storm occurred in 1880, and is still remembered as the "Marshfield tornado." Cf. my *We Always Lie to Strangers* (1951, p. 190). For a related tale see Allsopp (*Folklore of Romantic Arkansas*, 1931, II, p. 310). Cf. *Western Folklore*, XIV, 1 (January, 1955), p. 24. (V.R.)

THE WELL DIGGER

Told by Mr. Lon Jordan, Farmington, Ark., December, 1941. Cf. the tale which Botkin (*Treasury of Western Folklore*, 1951 p. 458) got from Levette J. Davidson, Denver, Colo. (V.R.)

This is the second American version reported of Motif K 474, "Trickster cheats rescuers into digging his well." Professor Davidson's Colorado version (originally published in *California Folklore Quarterly*, V [1946], 343–44) was the first. Stith Thompson cites only a version from Esthonia. The story is also known in Ireland. See Ó Súilleabháin, *Handbook of Irish Folklore*, p. 642, No. 30. (H.H.)

LOOSENING WEEDS

Told by Mr. Frank Hembree, Galena, Mo., September, 1944. He said it was a true story. (V.R.)

THE WICKED STEPMOTHER

Told by Mrs. Rose Spaulding, Eureka Springs, Ark., October, 1951. She had it from a little girl near Cassville, Mo. Cf. *Western Folklore*, XIV, 1 (January, 1955), pp. 26–27. (V.R.)

This is one of the forms of Type 780, "The Singing Bone," better known in America in the closely related ballad, "The Twa Sisters" (Child 10). In his treatment of the ballad, F. J. Child (*The English and Scottish Popular Ballads*, Boston, 1882, I, 118–41) includes some discussion of the equivalent popular tales (pp. 124–26). A version of the ballad in prose is given by J. Jacobs (*English Fairy Tales*, New York and London, 1893, pp. 42–47, No. 9). I have not seen the chief modern study of this folktale by Lutz Mackensen

(*Der singende Knochen,* FF Communications No. 49, Helsinki, 1923), but S. Thompson (*The Folktale,* New York, 1946, p. 136) has a brief discussion of Mackensen's work.

Few versions of this tale have been reported from English-speaking whites, although the comparable ballad is very well known. In a version from Derbyshire, England, given in S. O. Addy (*Household Tales,* London and Sheffield, 1895, pp. 42–43) a maid, irritated by a little girl's repeated request for her golden cup, kills her. The girl's spirit appears to her grieving mother and asks for the cup. An eastern Kentucky version given by L. Roberts (*South from Hell-fer-Sartin: Kentucky Mountain Tales,* Lexington, 1955, pp. 96–97) has the girl killed by her mother over a pear. In his notes, pp. 238–39, Professor Roberts discusses a second variant he has collected. In my folklore archive I have a west Kentucky version in which the girl is killed over the loss of three golden pears. The text has, however, a scary story ending. An Irish version is listed in Ó Súilleabháin, *Handbook of Irish Folklore,* Dublin, 1942, p. 574.

Negro versions of the tale are given by Parsons, (*Antilles,* III, 114–17), with excellent comparative headnotes to Nos. 123 and 125. Tales under Nos. 124 and 125 are closest to the Kentucky versions. The Negro version given by Johnson (*Journal of American Folklore,* XXXIV, 70–71) from Antigua, British West Indies, is one of the few English texts that fits completely the standard description of Type 780; a brother kills and buries his sister; a shepherd finds a bone like a flute, which reveals the murder when he plays on it. In the Kentucky, South Carolina, and Bahaman versions, the mother or stepmother is the murderer. In this, and in several other details, they resemble Type 720, "My Mother Slew Me; My Father Ate Me."

The relationship between the English and American versions of these two tale types will require further analysis. See "Pennywinkle! Pennywinkle!" in Randolph, *Who Blowed Up the Church House?* pp. 53–54, for an Ozark version of Type 720. To my notes for that story, given on p. 195, add the following: Lowrimore (*California Folklore Quarterly,* IV, 154–55) from California, but learned in Arkansas; Dobie (*Publications of the Texas Folk-Lore*

183

Society, VI, 53–54) from Texas, notes and introduction only, but interestingly close to the Lowrimore text; L. Roberts (*South from Hell-fer-Sartin,* pp. 91–93) from Kentucky; two other Kentucky mountain versions are mentioned on pp. 235–36. A Yorkshire text is given in an unexpected source—in the *Notes* to W. H. Jones and L. L. Kropf (*The Folk-Tales of the Magyars,* London, 1889, pp. 418–20). For two other Yorkshire texts see Addy (*Folk-Lore,* VIII, 394–95) and R. Blakeborough (*Wit, Character, Folklore & Customs of the North Riding of Yorkshire,* London, 1898, pp. 273–76). A fragmentary text is reprinted from "Notes and Queries" by Gutch and Peacock (*Examples of Printed Folk-Lore Concerning Lincolnshire,* London, 1908, p. 325). The only Irish reference I have located is a strange fragment in cantefable form given with a tune by P. W. Joyce (*Old Irish Folk Music and Songs,* New York and Dublin, 1909, p. 55). Apart from the song stanza the author recalls only that in the story a little boy is changed by enchantment into a white duck, and in this disguise is killed and eaten by his family. (H.H.)

BLIND DATE ON BULL CREEK

Told by Mr. Lew Beardon, Branson, Mo., December, 1938. He says that such tricks were common in the early days. Compare the stunt reported by Amos Harlin (*For Here Is My Fortune,* 1946, pp. 90–91) from Howell county, Mo. According to Associated Press accounts (March 1, 1951) a college student was drowned near Natchitoches, La., when he ran off a bluff into the Red River, after his classmates played "the irate husband prank" on him. Cf. Hennig Cohen's description of "Going to See the Widow" (*Journal of American Folklore,* 64 [1951], p. 223) as practiced in South Carolina; the same journal (pp. 420–21) carries a similar story from Alabama, reported by Eli Sobel. The same tale appears in H. Allen Smith (*The Compleat Practical Joker,* 1953, p. 81), but he calls it "The Brakeman's Daughter." John O'Hara (*Collier's,* Nov. 12, 1954, p. 6) says the boys used to play this joke at Pottsville, Pa. Cf. *Western Folklore,* XIV, 1 (January, 1955), pp. 27–28. (V.R.)

For a Kentucky version by one of my students see Penick (*Midwest Folklore,* III [1953], 175–76). In my folklore archive I have one version from Tennessee, and several others from Kentucky. For a Nevada version, "Going to See the O'Reilly Sisters," see Grotegut (*Western Folklore,* 14 [1955], 51–52). A somewhat similar hoax from Wisconsin was reported by Starr (*Journal of American Folklore,* 67 [1954], 184). (H.H.)

THE HOLLERING STORY

Told by Mr. Ed Wall, Pineville, Mo., April, 1922. Yarns of this type seem flat in print, but are much more effective when the dialogue is shouted at the top of the narrator's voice. Cf. a condensed version of this item in my *Funny Stories About Hillbillies* (1944, p. 14). (V.R.)

In a Massachusetts version given by J. C. Allen (*Tales and Trails of Martha's Vineyard,* Boston, 1938, pp. 92–93) a man's daughter is pregnant. Her father tells his neighbor the latter's son is responsible. In reply the neighbor ejaculates, "Nathan is the most careless cuss that ever drew the breath of life! Just this morning he busted a hoe-handle for me!" Botkin (*Treasury of New England Folklore,* p. 188) quotes a variant of the liar retort. When a deacon asks, "Do you mean to call me a liar?", he gets the calm reply, "No, Deacon, I don't. But ain't ye?"

It may be that the pattern of the hollering story is found in the South rather than the North. At any rate Vincent (*Here in Tennessee,* p. 26) gives an east Tennessee story in which a politician yells to a man plowing, "I heard you been telling all these folks I'm a no-good somebody." The plowman shouts back, "No, I don't know how they found it out." Folklore collectors should check how widely this "hollering story" pattern is known in other sections of this country. (H.H.)

IT JUST SUITS ME

Told by Mr. Joe Ingenthron, Forsyth, Mo., June, 1940. It has been attributed to James G. Blaine (A. R. Spofford's *Library of Wit and Humor,* Philadelphia, 1899, IV, 362). Cf. the anecdote related by Joe M. Evans (*A Corral Full of Stories,* El Paso, Texas, 1939, p. 48), and reprinted by Botkin (*Treasury of Western Folklore,* 1951, p. 15). The crack about Methodists and loose women turns up in many backwoods tales; see my *Funny Stories About Hillbillies* (1944, p. 11). Cf. *Western Folklore,* XIV, 1 (January, 1955), pp. 28–29. (V.R.)

There is a Tennessee version of this story in my folklore archive. This is a modern American (distant) relative of Type 1000, "Bargain Not To Become Angry." (H.H.)

THE BIG BLACK BOOGER

Told by Mrs. Rose Spaulding, Eureka Springs, Ark., November, 1951. She had it from her grandfather, who lived in Carroll county, Ark., in the 1880s. Cf. a related "Raw Head and Bloody Bones" tale in my *Ozark Superstitions* (1947, pp. 235–36). See *Western Folklore,* XIV, 1 (January, 1955), p. 29. (V.R.)

This story is one of two branches of Motif H 1411.1, "Fear test: staying in haunted house where corpse drops piecemeal down chimney." Usually tales in this group can be classified under Type 326, "The Boy Who Wanted to Learn What Fear Was."

In many of the following Negro texts the boy is rewarded for his bravery by getting the ghost's hidden treasure. See: *Journal of American Folklore,* XII, 64–65 (an Alabama text reprinted from *Southern Workman* for March 1898); Parsons, *Journal of American Folklore,* XXX, 195, note 2 (North Carolina); *Journal of American Folklore,* 217 (Virginia); Bacon and Parsons, *Journal of American Folklore,* XXXV, 290 (Virginia); Fauset, *Journal of American Folklore,* XLI, 543 (Pennsylvania, from Virginia); E. C. Parsons, *Folk-Lore of the Sea Islands, South Carolina,* Cambridge and New York, 1923, p. 126. An Irish version is given in P. Kennedy, *Legendary Fictions of the Irish Celts,* London and New York, 1891, pp. 137–40.

The branch of this piecemeal corpse-assembly yarn to which this Ozark tale belongs, as Mr. Randolph's version clearly demonstrates, is not that of a fear test, but rather a story to scare children. In this form with the dialogue about the parts of the body,

186

it has been reported from white informants by Boggs, *Journal of American Folklore,* XLVII, 296–97, Version B (from North Carolina); R. Chambers, *Popular Rhymes of Scotland,* London and Edinburgh, 1870, pp. 64–66. Chambers' text "much Anglicised" is given in J. Jacobs, *English Fairy Tales,* 2d ed., revised, New York and London, 1893, pp. 179–82, No. 32. Mr. Jacobs' version has been frequently used in children's books. (H.H.)

BIG FRAID AND LITTLE FRAID

Told by Mrs. Betrenia Bowker, Kansas City, Mo., September, 1951. She got it from Mr. Johnny Stalter, at Pierce City, Mo., in the 1930s. Compare Grace Partridge Smith (*Southern Folklore Quarterly,* VI, 2 [1942], p. 89), also Emrich and Korson (*Child's Book of Folklore,* 1947, p. 211). There is a similar tale in the *Bulletin of the Missouri Historical Society* (VI [July, 1950], 479–80) from Fayette, Mo. Compare *Midwest Folklore,* VI, 1 (Spring, 1956), 41–42. See Dorson (*Negro Folktales in Michigan,* 1956, pp. 187–88) who identifies it as Motif K 1671.1 in Baughman's index. (V.R.)

Smith (*Southern Folklore Quarterly,* VI, 89–94) was the first to point out the European affiliations of this tale which is quite popular in America. Full references will be given in my forthcoming New Jersey collection. It will probably be recognized by a motif number in the new edition of the *Motif Index.* (H.H.)
[Herbert Halpert's annotations to this book were completed before the publication of Dorson's *Negro Folktales in Michigan.* Ed.]

THE WISE MAN'S QUESTIONS

Told by Miss Callista O'Neill, Day, Mo., September, 1941. Several versions, she said, were current among her neighbors on Bear Creek, in Taney county, Mo. Cf. a related tale in Jackson's *On a Slow Train Through Arkansaw* (1903, pp. 57–58). See *Western Folklore,* XIV, 1 (January, 1955), pp. 30–31. (V.R.)

This is a modernized version of an international tale, Type 922, "The Shepherd Substituting for the Priest Answers the King's Questions." It is fairly well known in the British tradition, but has not been reported frequently from the United States. The story has the same plot as the ballad "King John and the Bishop" (Child 45). There is a good discussion of the related tales and ballads in F. J. Child (*The English and Scottish Popular Ballads,* 1884, I, 403–14). A version of the ballad is retold in prose form by J. Jacobs (*More English Fairy Tales,* London, 1894, pp. 146–49, No. 72). I have been unable to consult the definitive study of the tale by Walter Anderson (*Kaiser und Abt,* Folklore Fellows Communications, No. 42; Helsinki, 1923). See S. Thompson (*The Folktale,* New York, 1946, pp. 161–62, and 432–33) for discussion of both the tale and Anderson's study. In versions of the tale there is considerable variation both in the characters and in the questions.

North American versions have been published by Barry (*Journal of American Folklore,* XXI, 58–59) from a Fulton, Missouri native, but collected in New Jersey; Fauset (*Journal of American Folklore,* XL, 259–60) from a Mississippi Negro; Johnson (*Journal of American Folklore,* XXXIV, 74), a Negro text from Antigua, British West Indies; A. H. Fauset (*Folklore from Nova Scotia,* New York, 1931, pp. 53–54) from Dartmouth, Nova Scotia; E. C. Parsons (*Folk-Lore from the Cape Verde Islands,* Cambridge and New York, 1923, I, 94–95), two versions collected in New England from Portuguese-speaking Negroes. To round out the American record on this story, Professor Edwin C. Kirkland has three unpublished texts: a South Carolina version, and two from Florida. I heard a version of the story in the Catskill Mountain region of New York, but have only incomplete notes on it. The story was familiar to a middle-aged woman from western Kentucky, but she could not give me the text.

According to F. W. Chandler (*The Literature of Roguery,* Boston and New York, 1907, I, 69), the story is given in Humphrey Crouch's *England's Jests Refin'd* (1687). Other English versions are given by E. M. Leather (*The Folklore of Herefordshire,* Hereford and London, 1912, pp. 177–78), and by Wilson (*Folk-Lore,* XLIX, 182–83) from Westmorland, but learned from a traveling Scotchman. Scottish versions of the tale are reported in

J. F. Campbell (*Popular Tales of the West Highlands,* Edinburgh, 1862, II, 391–92), J. E. Simpkins (*Examples of Printed Folklore Concerning Fife,* London, 1914, pp. 250–51), and from the Scottish Hebrides by M. F. Shaw (*Folksongs and Folklore of South Uist,* London, 1955, pp. 62–63). (H.H.)

FIDDLER'S CAVE

Told by Mrs. Jean Lightfoot Kappell, West Milton, Ohio, October, 1951. She heard it in Greene county, Mo., about 1930. This yarn is common in Ozark, Howell, Stone, and Taney counties, in southwest Missouri. One version, without any mention of the girl, was published anonymously in the Springfield, Mo., *News & Leader,* April 30, 1938. Cf. *Western Folklore,* XIV, 1 (January, 1955), p. 30. (V.R.)

As far as I know, Kentucky is the only other state from which versions of the legend of a fiddler lost in a cave have been reported. I am indebted to Dr. Hensley C. Woodbridge for calling my attention to two texts: Mattingly Spalding (*Bardstown, Town of Tradition,* Baltimore, 1942, reprinted 1947, pp. 78–79), and, from the same area, a newspaper article by J. S. Wilson, "Bardstown's Quaint Sights . . . A Cave and Its Gruesome Legend," *The Kentucky Standard,* Bardstown, Ky., Jan. 13, 1955. According to an editorial note, Wilson's story "appeared in the Louisville *Courier-Journal* shortly after 1900." These two Bardstown texts, reprinted by me in *Kentucky Folklore Record,* II, 99–101, 1956, vary slightly from each other; but both resemble a common British form of the legend in that the lost fiddler entered the cave to explore it. On dark nights fiddle music can still be heard from underground. Two of my Kentucky students have contributed texts of the legend to my folklore archive. Professor D. K. Wilgus has other (Bardstown) versions in his folklore archive.

Legends about a fiddler or piper (in single versions a man with a horn or a drum) who is lost in a cave or underground passage (compare Motif F 721.1, "Underground passages") are found in all parts of the British Isles. Since I am still trying both to learn if the legend is known elsewhere in Europe and to work out the relationship between the various legends, I am limiting my references to a few major studies and collections. See: W. L. Manson (*The Highland Bagpipe, Its History, Literature and Music,* Paisley and London, 1901, pp. 247–56); F. Tolmie (*Journal of the Folk-Song Society,* IV, No. 16, pp. 157–60); A. A. MacGregor (*The Peat-Fire Flame: Folk-Tales and Traditions of the Highlands & Islands,* Edinburgh and London, 1947, pp. 167–69); A. Martin Freeman (*Journal of the Welsh Folk-Song Society,* III, Part 3, No. 2, pp. 142–45).

The comment in Mr. Randolph's story that on the third morning it sounded "like the fiddle was under water" also connects this legend with legends of the drowned musician whose music can still be heard on certain occasions. (H.H.)

THE HOLY ROLLERS

Told by Miss Fay Stubbs, Springfield, Mo., December, 1951. Holy Rollers often fall to the floor, apparently unconscious. Sometimes, as May Kennedy McCord has observed (Springfield, Mo., *News & Leader,* Jan. 29, 1932), "cloaks and wraps are very kindly thrown across their limbs." Amos Harlin (*For Here Is My Fortune,* 1946, pp. 70–71) tells of a worshiper in Howell county, Mo., who rushed through the crowd "with stark nakedness only one button away." Homer Croy (*What Grandpa Laughed At,* 1948, p. 29) credits a similar tale to "a traveling evangelist in the Ozarks," and it is reprinted by Otto Ernest Rayburn (*Ozark Guide* [Winter, 1949], p. 28). Everett Webber tells me he heard the same story, related as an actual occurrence near Blue Eye, Mo., in the 1940s. See Randolph and Wilson (*Down in the Holler,* 1953, p. 39). (V.R.)

A LITTLE MORE CIDER

Told by Mr. Bob Wyrick, Eureka Springs, Ark., October, 1948. The cider sellers lived near Berryville, Ark., he says, about 1920. (V.R.)

190

THE SPANISH BURIAL

Told by Mr. Elbert Short, Crane, Mo., June, 1933. Mr. Short heard reports of this stunt in several south Missouri towns about 1914. Cf. my *Funny Stories About Hillbillies* (1944, p. 22); also *Midwest Folklore*, VI, 1 (Spring, 1956), pp. 40–41. (V.R.)

Davy Crockett (*The Life of Davy Crockett,* Signet Book S 1214, New York, 1955, pp. 196–97) was given a report of this as a popular trick played on greenhorns in notorious Natchez-under-the-hill. The man trapped had to treat all hands. Saxon, Dreyer and Tallant (*Gumbo Ya-Ya,* p. 344) reprint an old New Orleans newspaper report of this initiation hoax played on Negro newcomers in prison. (H.H.)

TO HELL WITH JOPLIN

Told by an elderly gentleman in Carroll county, Ark., July, 1948. It is a true story, he says. (V.R.)

WE CALL IT LAPLAND

Told by Mr. Marcus Freck, Beardstown, Ill., August, 1925. He heard it at Hot Springs, Ark., about 1898. Cf. Marion Hughes (*Three Years in Arkansaw,* 1904, pp. 29–30); Mrs. J. K. Hudson (*In the Missouri Woods,* 1905, p. 43); Dallas T. Herndon (*Centennial History of Arkansas,* 1922, I, 398); Allsopp (*Folklore of Romantic Arkansas,* 1931, II, pp. 262–64); Masterson (*Tall Tales of Arkansaw,* 1943, pp. 103, 337); Mirandy Bauersfeld (*Breezes from Persimmon Holler,* 1943, p. 192); and Fred High (*Forty-Three Years for Uncle Sam,* 1949, p. 8). (V.R.)

In a text contributed to my folklore archive, one of my students reported that in 1901 her father was a minister in Kennett, Dunklin county, Mo., and heard a different explanation of the origin of "the boot" of Missouri. When the line was being made, an old man who owned a great deal of the section "asked that his place be left in Missouri—as he had always heard it was so sickly in Arkansas." A variant of this version of the tale is given in Allsopp, *Folklore of Romantic Arkansas,* II, p. 262. (H.H.)

Told by Mrs. Emma L. Dusenbury, Mena, Ark., April, 1938. She had it from a Missourian in the 1880s. I have heard several other versions of this tale, but most of them are unprintable. (V.R.)

This seems to be a much-localized version of Type 1423, Motif K 1518, "The enchanted pear tree." The type form of the story is given in *The Decameron* of Boccaccio (seventh day, ninth tale). In the standard form of the story the magical performance is part of the deceit played on the cuckold husband by his wife and her lover. But it is a farmer's daughter and his hired hand who trick the farmer in a New Mexican version given by Zunser (*Journal of American Folklore*, XLVIII [1935], 177–78). (H.H.)

SHE'S GOT ONE SPOILED TIT!

Told by Mrs. Ethel Barnes, Hot Springs, Ark., April, 1938. She thought it dated at least to 1885. Marion Hughes (*Three Years in Arkansaw*, 1904, pp. 39–40) published this one, and Masterson (*Tall Tales of Arkansaw*, 1943, p. 98) reprinted it. The old-timers say that the tale was current long before the turn of the century, and scoff at the idea that Hughes "made it up." (V.R.)

This is a version of Type 1698, "Deaf Persons and their Foolish Answers." In an Irish version (Ó Súilleabháin, *Handbook of Irish Folklore*, p. 644, No. 63), while the priest is praying for a dead parishioner, the deaf man stands up to describe his strayed sow. (H.H.)

THE YANK REUNION

Told by Mr. Farwell Gould, Pittsburg, Kansas, June, 1929. He heard it in Arkansas, about 1880. Jackson (*On a Slow Train Through Arkansaw*, 1903, pp. 72–74) has a similar tale of a reunion somewhere in Missouri. Cf. L. B. Williams (*Master Book of Humorous Illustrations*, New York, 1938, p. 365). (V.R.)

Dobie (*Publications of the Texas Folklore Society*, XXI, 3–4) gives a South Carolina version of this story in which a former Confederate general makes a similar remark about a G.A.R. veteran.

The story is not limited to the Civil War. In a post–Spanish-American War version given by E. C. Lewis (*After Dinner Stories,* New York and Boston, 1905, p. 38), a Spaniard drops five dollars into the cup of a badly injured veteran saying, "You're the first American I've seen since the war that was done up to suit me." The story can be used to express antinational or antireligious feeling, as in Nova Scotian versions given by A. H. Fauset (*Folklore from Nova Scotia,* New York, 1931, pp. 56–57). The second version has a crippled Jewish soldier, but the first has no war connection: an Irishman says a crippled Englishman is the first "trimmed to suit me." I suspect this story has a wide distribution, serving to express the antagonism between various regional, national, or religious groups. (H.H.)

OLD MAN PRICE'S BOAR

Told by Mr. Ed Wall, Pineville, Mo., April, 1922. He said it was a true story. Related tales about the odor of old boars and sows in heat are not uncommon. This kind of deadpan insinuation gets a laugh from any backwoods audience. Cf. Randolph & Wilson (*Down in the Holler,* 1953, p. 195); also *Midwest Folklore,* VI, 1 (Spring, 1956) pp. 46–47.

THE TWO WHITE SPRINGS

Told by Mr. Frank Hembree, Galena, Mo., April, 1945. Mr. Hembree heard it near Galena, about 1906. For information about this riddle see Archer Taylor (*Southern Folklore Quarterly,* VIII [1944], 23–25). Cf. *Western Folklore* XIV, 1 (January, 1955), p. 26. (V.R.)

THEY ALL STARTED FROM SCRATCH

Told by Mr. Walter J. Hazlewood, Eureka Springs, Ark., August, 1950. (V.R.)

A very similar version (Anon., *Funny Side Up,* New York, 1952, p. 165) differs only in minor details. The wealthy man has his six married sons join him for dinner, and announces a bonus of $10,000 for the first grandchild. He bows his head to give the blessing; when he looks up, he is the only one left at the table. (H.H.)

PINKLEY WAS A FOOL

Told by Mr. J. H. McGee, Joplin, Mo., July, 1934. He heard it near Sparta, Mo., about 1900. This tale is sometimes linked to John A. Murrell, a highwayman who terrorized eastern Arkansas in the 1840s. Cf. Allsopp, *Folklore of Romantic Arkansas,* 1931, I, 302); also William Yancey Shackleford, *Gun-Fighters of the Old West,* 1943, p. 6; and *Midwest Folklore,* VI, 1 (Spring, 1956) 42–43. (V.R.)

There are a variety of tales about men who are taken to be wealthy and are killed, or have narrow escapes from being murdered. In a Texas legend given by Dobie in *Publications of the Texas Folklore Society,* XIII, 46, a settler carrying a rattling chain in his saddlebags is killed because the murderer thinks he is carrying gold or silver. In a Pennsylvania legend reported by G. Korson, *Minstrels of the Mine Patch,* Philadelphia, 1938, pp. 161–64, the jingle of coins in a peddler's saddlebags brought about his murder. Instead of finding a fortune in the saddlebags, the murderer gets nothing but a small sum in copper coins. In a Kentucky story given in Bradley, *Stories and Speeches of William O. Bradley,* p. 27, a man wearing elegant clothes and a glossy silk hat escaped death because one of the gang rightly estimated that the intended victim had invested all his money in the purchase of his hat. (H.H.)

WOMEN RUN WITH THE WOLVES

Told by Mr. Ed Wall, Pineville, Mo., April, 1922. Such talk was common, he says, among hunters and trappers along the Cowskin River in the 1890s. Cf. the "Lobo Girl" story recorded by

194

L. D. Bertillion (*Publications of the Texas Folklore Society,* XIII [1937], pp. 79–85). Bertillion's tale is reprinted by Botkin (*Treasury of American Folklore,* 1944, pp. 758–63). See also the "Wolf Boy" story reported by Mary Celestia Parler (*Arkansas Folklore,* VI, 2 [1956], p. 4). Compare *Midwest Folklore* VI, 1 (Spring, 1956), 38–39. (V.R.)

Some interesting, world-wide motifs are involved in this story. In Vol. I of the revised edition of Thompson's *Motif-Index,* see Motifs B 453.3, "Helpful wolf"; B 535, "Animal nurse"; B 634, "Monstrous offspring from animal marriage"; B 635.2, "Wolf boy [girl] running around with wolf and cubs recovered. . . ." (H.H.)

THE SILENT RIFLE

Told by Mr. Farwell Gould, Pittsburg, Kan., April, 1930. He heard it near Batesville, Ark., in the 1860s. Perry Mason (Springfield, Mo., *News,* Dec. 28, 1951) tells a similar story of his grandfather's experience in the Civil War. (V.R.)

JACK AND THE GOWER

Told by Mr. William Hatton, Columbia, Mo., July, 1929. He heard it in Lawrence county, Mo., about 1905. Mr. Hatton's informant was born in Searcy county, Ark., about 1880. A fabulous reptile called the gowrow is reported from many places in the Ozarks; see my *We Always Lie to Strangers* (1951, pp. 41–46). Margaret J. Adams of Omaha, Neb., who went to school in Benton county, Ark., tells me that *garou* is the proper spelling. (V.R.)

This is a very much reduced version of Type 300, "The Dragon Slayer." For discussion of this tale, which is frequently found in conjunction with other tale types, see Stith Thompson's *The Folktale* (New York, 1946), pp. 24–25.

In the usual *Märchen* form the hero has a magical weapon to kill the dragon. The silver bullet used to kill the monster in Mr. Randolph's version is the standard device for counteracting witchcraft. It is worth observing that in the Ozarks magical details of a fairy-tale kind tend to be replaced by the more familiar magic

195

of legendary belief, i.e., devil lore and/or witchcraft. See for example the title story in Randolph, *The Devil's Pretty Daughter*. (H.H.)

HE WASN'T MY SON-IN-LAW

Told by Mr. Otto Ernest Rayburn, Eureka Springs, Ark., December, 1948. Compare Bennett Cerf (*Anything for a Laugh,* 1946, p. 75). Rayburn printed a shorter version in his quarterly *Ozark Guide* (Summer, 1949, p. 41). In *Fun Fare, Reader's Digest Wit and Humor* (Pleasantville, N.Y., 1949, p. 214) this story is credited to the *Wall Street Journal*. (V.R.)

See: Anon., *Funny Side Up* (New York, 1952), p. 5, for a very similar text. (H.H.)

THE GHOST WAS STILL MAD

Told by Mrs. Marie Wilbur, Pineville, Mo., October, 1929. She had it from Mrs. Lucinda Mosier, also of Pineville. Cf. my *Ozark Ghost Stories* (1944, p. 12); also a reference in *Ozark Superstitions* (1947, pp. 222–23). (V.R.)

GOD DAMN THE WIND

Told by Mr. H. F. Walker, Joplin, Mo., September, 1923. He credited it to "a hillbilly family" from eastern Oklahoma. This is an example of what the Ozarker calls a "build-up" story. Joseph Carrière (*Tales from the French Folklore of Missouri*, 1937, pp. 310–11) found a similar yarn among the Missouri Creoles. Cf. *Midwest Folklore*, VI, 1 (Spring, 1956) 45–46. (V.R.)

All formula tales have been much neglected by collectors in this country. This delightfully mad version of a cumulative tale clearly belongs under Type 2030, "The Old Woman and Her Pig." In his classification of formula tales, Taylor (*Journal of American Folklore*, XLVI, 84) lists such tales as "Chains with interdependent members," and gives a bibliography of studies. An English text is given in a study of cumulative tales by W. H. Clouston (*Popular Tales and Fictions*, Edinburgh and London, 1887, I, 289–313). Emenau (*Journal of American Folklore*, LV,

196

272–88) studied fourteen versions of "The Old Woman and Her Pig" from India. Parsons, *Antilles,* III, pp. 314–15, No. 333 gives several versions and supplementary notes. There are also some useful notes on the tale in Dobie (*Publications of the Texas Folklore Society,* VI, 55).

I am not giving here a full list of the many American, English, Scottish and Irish versions of "The Old Woman and Her Pig," because I can find none that are really close to Mr. Randolph's text. It may be worth noting, however, that at least two versions, one from Ontario, Canada, given by Wintemberg (*Journal of American Folklore,* XXXI, 117–19) and one from Yorkshire in R. Blakeborough (*Wit, Character, Folklore & Customs of the North Riding of Yorkshire,* London, 1898, pp. 263–65) have the wind as the turning point of the cumulative series. (H.H.)

THE LOOKING GLASS

Told by Mr. Jack Short, Galena, Mo., February, 1940. Cf. the story quoted by Pearl Spurlock (*Over the Old Ozark Trails,* Branson, Mo., 1936, p. 25), who says, "A great many of these natives, especially the older generation, have never seen a looking glass." A similar item appears in L. B. Williams (*Master Book of Humorous Illustrations,* New York, 1938, p. 354). Bennett Cerf (*Anything for a Laugh,* 1946, p. 158) says that Fibber McGee has been getting laughs with this story for twenty years. (V.R.)

Although infrequently reported, this yarn has a surprisingly wide distribution. In a localized cowboy variant of this tale given by Thorp and Clark (*Partner of the Wind,* p. 209), the man (quite sober) admires "the picture" in the mirror. His wife finds the mirror, looks at it, and then smashes it over her husband's head with the remark, "So *that's* the sour-faced hussy you've been chasin', is it!" Apparently it is well known in Kentucky. Two variants have appeared in Allan M. Trout's column, "Greetings," Louisville *Courier-Journal,* July 9, 1955 and Dec. 13, 1955; and there is a third text in my folklore archive. Wilson (*Folk-Lore,* XLIX [1938], 277–78) gives a version from Westmorland, England, and mentions that there are Irish and Chinese versions.

197

An amusingly elaborated Korean version is reprinted by E. E. Edwards (*Bamboo, Lotus and Palm,* London, 1948, pp. 319–21). In it a young wife thinks her reflection in the mirror must be the picture of a new concubine that her husband has acquired; he looks at it and thinks his wife has a lover. In turn mother-in-law, father-in-law and then the whole village become embroiled, including the town magistrate, who thinks he sees the picture of an official sent by the government to replace him. Finally a bright young junior official points out that the mirror reflects the face of each one who looks at it. Another Korean version given by Kim So-Un (*The Story Bag: A Collection of Korean Folk Tales,* Rutland, Vt., and Tokyo, Japan, c. 1955, pp. 44–50) closely resembles the Chinese example given in W. Eberhard (*Chinese Fairy Tales and Folk Tales,* London, 1937, p. 265). (H.H.)

HARVEY AND MYRA

Told by Dr. O. St. John, Pineville, Mo., December, 1922. Cf. my *Funny Stories About Hillbillies* (1944, p. 10); also J. M. Elgart (*Over Sexteen,* 1951, p. 58). (V.R.)

FOUR ACES AIN'T GOOD

Told by Mr. Ern Long, Joplin, Mo., August, 1931. I have heard several versions of this tale in southern Missouri, always related as true stories. (V.R.)

TOBEY THE KING SNAKE

Told by Mrs. Ethel Barnes, Hot Springs, Ark., April, 1938. She had it from relatives who lived near Hot Springs in the 1880s. For related items see my *Ozark Superstitions* (1947, pp. 255–56); also *We Always Lie to Strangers* (1951, pp. 141–42). Cf. H. P. Beck's "Herpetological Lore from the Blue Ridge" (*Midwest Folklore,* II [1952], 146–47). (V.R.)

The chief motif in this story, E 105, "Resuscitation by herbs (leaves)" is part of Type 612, "The Three Snake Leaves." A Negro story originally from Tennessee, "De Snakes an' de Quare Weed," was collected in Missouri by M. A. Owen (*Voodoo Tales,*

New York and London, 1893, pp. 253–57). In this tale a man observed how a snake that he had cut in two was brought back to life by a weed put on the corpse by its mate. When the scythe the man was carrying almost cut his neck in two, the dying man's hand went up to his neck. The piece of weed held in that hand healed the wound and restored him to life. His blood-drenched collar proved to him it was not a dream. This Tennessee version is closer than the Arkansas one to the type form of the story. I recall reading other stories in which a snake or animal, bitten in a fight with a poisonous snake, eats a weed and then returns to the fight, but I cannot give specific references. (H.H.)

HELL AMONG THE CHICKENS

Told by Mr. Charles Thomas, Pittsburg, Kan., November, 1934. He got it from a farmer near Milo, in Barton county, Mo. A similar tale appeared in the Lamar, Mo., *Democrat* (Jan. 26, 1940), credited to Charles J. Huckleberry. Cf. the variant reported by Joe and Frank Wig (*Ree-laxin' at Skranky Knob,* Hannibal, Mo., 1948, pp. 10–13). Cf. Otho Pratt (*Gensang Jones' Ozark Tales,* 1951, p. 79) and Will Rice (*Arkansas Gazette,* Sept. 8, 1952). Mr. Dick Simpson, Eureka Springs, Ark., in September, 1953, told me this tale as a true story; he got it from Ed Williams, a banker at Bald Knob, Ark., who said it happened near Shirley, Ark. (V.R.)

A version of this story is used to explain how a certain motion picture studio worker in Hollywood got his nickname of "Cold Nose." See Allen, *Western Folklore,* XIII (1953), 11. In 1955 a preacher in Murray, Kentucky, told me a variant of this story. (H.H.)

GABE SAYS IT AIN'T SO BAD

Told by Mrs. Marie Wilbur, Pineville, Mo., November, 1929. She had it from her father in McDonald county, Mo. John F. Dunckel (*The Mollyjoggers,* Springfield, Mo., n.d., p. 18) prints a related yarn, as recited near Springfield about 1900. (V.R.)

This is a version of Type 2014, "The House Is Burned Down."

See versions in Schermerhorn (*Schermerhorn's Stories,* p. 359); and Hazlitt (*New London Jest Book,* pp. 43–44). The latter text also appears in another book by Hazlitt (*Studies in Jocular Literature,* pp. 84–85). A modern Colorado tale given by Martin (*Hoosier Folklore,* VII [1948], 21) involves a plane, a parachute, and a haystack, and has a similar alternation between "that's good" and "that's bad." (H.H.)

THE BOOGER DOG

Told by Mr. D. A. Hicks, Kansas City, Mo., December, 1935. See the references to supernatural black dogs in my *Ozark Superstitions* (1947, pp. 224–25, 275). Cf. Charles Carson's novel *Mountain Troubadour* (1951, pp. 148–49). (V.R.)

Thompson (*Body, Boots & Britches,* Philadelphia, 1940, p. 150) gives a "lying tale" version from New York about a cat with its head chopped off which carried its head in its mouth. I have unpublished versions from northern New Jersey and southwestern Tennessee in my folklore archive. A southern New Jersey version in my forthcoming collection is also about a cat. It resembles Mr. Randolph's text, however, in having supernatural associations since it is one of the feats ascribed to a trickster magician. Loomis (*California Folklore Quarterly,* IV, 128) mentions an Irish saint who "could swim the sea with his head in his teeth." (H.H.)

AN INNOCENT MAN

Told by Mrs. Mary Burke, Springfield, Mo., May, 1932. She heard it from her mother in Christian county, Mo., about 1891. Richard M. Dorson (*Journal of American Folklore,* 61 [1948], p. 138) reports a similar tale from Michigan. (V.R.)

GOOD COUNTRY BUTTERMILK

Told by Mrs. Mary Elizabeth Mahnkey, Mincy, Mo., October, 1943. She had it from her parents, who used to live in Harrison, Ark. (V.R.)

WHAT THEY TOLD ON JASPER

Told by Mr. Jack Short, Galena, Mo., February, 1940. He has a great store of these "fool boy" stories. Compare Lurie (*Make 'Em Laugh,* 1927, pp. 45, 121). See similar items in my *Funny Stories About Hillbillies* (1944, pp. 6, 11); also in *Who Blowed Up the Church House?* (1952, pp. 97–99). (V.R.)

PAW WON'T LIKE THIS

Told by Mr. Wiley Burns, Joplin, Mo., May, 1931. He heard it near Bentonville, Ark., about 1897. Dunckel (*The Mollyjoggers,* n.d., pp. 32–33) reports a similar yarn as current in Greene county, Mo., before 1905. See also Irvin S. Cobb (*A Laugh a Day Keeps the Doctor Away,* 1923, p. 238); Lurie, (*Make 'Em Laugh,* 1927, pp. 90–91) and Cerf (*Anything for a Laugh,* 1946, p. 145). Will Rice (*Arkansas Gazette,* June 10, 1952) says it happened "just the other day" near Damascus, Ark. (V.R.)

Other versions are given in Lewis (*After Dinner Stories,* New York and Boston, 1905, p. 71) and Schermerhorn (*Schermerhorn's Stories,* p. 154). Ford (*Thistledown,* p. 326) gives a related Scottish tale in which a boy asks a farmer for help with his overturned load of hay. Farmer doesn't want to interrupt his plowing—and boy finally says his father is underneath the load. Boatright (*Folk Laughter on the American Frontier,* p. 105) gives a political story used to "make the point that your opponent's assumptions are based on incomplete information." A traveler seeing a boy frantically scattering hay from an overturned load, tells him he should do it carefully. The boy points and says, "Dad's under there." (H.H.)

THE LAZY FARMER

Told by Mr. Ed Worden, Eureka Springs, Ark., October, 1948. (V.R.)

This story with the punch line "Is it shucked? [shelled?]" is very popular in America, and is also known in a closely related form in Haiti, Rumania and Turkey. Full references are given in my forthcoming New Jersey collection. The story will probably be included in the revised edition of the *Motif Index* under W 111, "Laziness." (H.H.)

A PRIVATE ROOM

Told by Mrs. Ann Miller, Aurora, Mo., March, 1950. She credited it to an innkeeper from Sedalia, Mo., who heard it in 1935. (V.R.)

In Schermerhorn (*Schermerhorn's Stories,* p. 194) a rural couple came to the city to celebrate their golden wedding anniversary. They are given a modern hotel suite with twin beds. The husband says he had hoped they could be alone that night. (H.H.)

BRAINS FOR A TANNER

Told by Mr. Price Paine, Noel, Mo., October, 1923. He heard it near Elk Springs, Mo., about 1898. Tales of wholesale vengeance are common in the Ozarks. J. A. Sturges (*History of McDonald County, Missouri,* Pineville, Mo., 1897, pp. 186–88) says that seventeen men were killed to avenge the murder of Mark Harmon, near the mouth of Elk Horn. For the use of human brains in tanning skins see the WPA guidebook *Idaho* (1937, pp. 395–96), Botkin's *Treasury of Western Folklore* (1951, pp. 658–59), and *The Ozarks Mountaineer* (Branson, Mo., I, 2 [April, 1952], p. 3). (V.R.)

Botkin (*Treasury of American Folklore,* p. 369) quotes a story in which a man says he had to kill six Texicans to get brains enough to tan a squirrel skin. (H.H.)

THEY MOVED THE GRAVEYARD

Told by Mr. T. A. McQuary, Galena, Mo., January, 1936. He thought it referred to the village of Linn Creek, Mo., submerged when the Bagnell Dam was built in 1930. Compare Bennett Cerf (*Anything for a Laugh,* 1946, pp. 58–59). (V.R.)

Davis (*Proceedings of the Vermont Historical Society,* V, 332) gives a Vermont version of this yarn of exaggerated understatement with the punch line "Well, Grandma didn't look what you'd call real rugged." Botkin (*Treasury of New England Folklore,* pp. 109–10) quotes both the Davis story and another Vermont version that has the final statement that Uncle John, seventy years dead, looked "kinda poorly." (H.H.)

YOCUM USED HIS HEAD

Told by Mr. Jack Short, Galena, Mo., February, 1940. He heard it near Hurley, Mo., in the 1890s. A similar tale appeared in the Kansas City *Times* (March 26, 1951) as the experience of Jacob Coonce, who lived in St. Clair county, Mo., about 1831. The *Times* story was reprinted in the *Missouri Historical Review* (October, 1951, p. 110). (V.R.)

A PICKARD NEVER FORGETS

Told by Mr. Franklin Allen, Eureka Springs, Ark., June, 1950. It was a true account, he said, of something that happened near Joplin, Mo. (V.R.)

THE CHILI KING

Told by Mr. Jim Tooley, Grove, Okla., December, 1945. He had it from his neighbors in Newton county, Mo. This is always related as a true story, but I have heard three different versions in Arkansas and Oklahoma. (V.R.)

TURTLES GROW FAST

Told by Mr. Farwell Gould, Pittsburg, Kan., February, 1930. He heard the story near Batesville, Ark., shortly after the Civil War. Cf. Hans Zinsser (*As I Remember Him,* Boston, 1940, pp. 178–79); B. C. Clough (*The American Imagination at Work,* New York, 1947, pp. 665–66); Homer Croy (*What Grandpa Laughed At,* 1948, pp. 239–40); and H. Allen Smith (*The Compleat Practical Joker,* 1953, pp. 195–96). (V.R.)

THE BOLSTER

Told by a drunken preacher in Hot Springs, Ark., March, 1938. He said it was a common story among backwoods folk about 1900.

Compare *Anecdota Americana* (1934, p. 154); my *Funny Stories About Hillbillies* (1944, p. 20); and Norman Lockridge (*Waggish Tales of the Czechs,* 1947, pp. 169–71). (V.R.)

Told by Mrs. Ethel Barnes, Hot Springs, Ark., April, 1938. She had it from people who lived in Garland county, Ark., about 1889. See Lucile Upton's column in the Springfield, Mo., *News* (Feb. 20, 1952) for a variant from Willow Springs, Mo. "This is supposed to have actually happened," writes Miss Upton's anonymous contributor. (V.R.)

The trick of "ghost-shamming," as one scholar has called it, is frequently reported in the American and British folk tradition. The reports are often so similar that I suspect we are frequently dealing with a folk legend rather than an actual report of a hoax. Perhaps it would be safer to say that reports of the hoax tend to follow legendary patterns. (H.H.)

TOM AND JERRY

Told by Mr. W. H. Johnson, Hollister, Mo., July, 1936. He credited it to one of his backwoods neighbors. Cf. Homer Croy (*What Grandpa Laughed At,* 1948, pp. 58–59). (V.R.)

This fable is often a part of Type 670, "The Animal Languages." In *The Arabian Nights* the Wazir tells a version of the full story to attempt to discourage Sharazad (Shaharazade) from marrying the bloodthirsty sultan. See *The Arabian Nights' Entertainment,* trans. by Richard F. Burton (Modern Library Edition, New York, 1923), pp. 14–21. The story is also part of the cycle of legends about King Solomon. See L. Ginzberg (*The Legends of the Jews,* Philadelphia, 1913, IV, 138–41), and the African version translated in St. John D. Seymour (*Tales of King Solomon,* London, 1924, pp. 102–4). Compare the Mexican version noted below.

In a Florida Negro version by Hurston (*Mules and Men,* pp. 154–55), the ox (who works teamed up with a mule) plays sick. The mule squeals on him, then reports to the ox that Ole Massa was talking to a butcher. As the ox is led off to slaughter, he threatens revenge—and since then rawhide is always used to whip mules. In a Mexican version by Guerra (*Publications of the Texas Folklore Society,* XVIII, 190–91) a horse recommends to a tired ox that it play sick. King Solomon, who overhears the dialogue, has the horse hitched to the plow and worked hard. That evening he hears the horse tell the ox that he overheard the driver say the ox would be killed the next day if he didn't recover. The ox promptly acts on the advice. In a New Mexican version given by Zunser (*Journal of American Folklore,* XLVIII, 158) a man who understands animal speech overhears the burro recommending to the ox that it rebel. When it does, the man promptly whips the burro for giving such advice. But a new theme is then introduced in the story, and we are not told more about the ox.

In different versions of Type 670, it is some other animal conversation that is overheard by the man. For additional references see E. C. Parsons (*Antilles,* III, p. 310, No. 322). (H.H.)

WILD PIGEONS

Told by Mr. L. S. Baynes, Fort Smith, Ark., June, 1929. He got the story from Pete Gantrot of Hot Springs, Ark., about 1895. Wild pigeons, now extinct, were extraordinarily numerous in the 1880s. Great flocks darkened the sky, and broke down big trees (Hoenshel, *Stories of the Pioneers,* Branson, Mo., 1915, p. 13). See my *We Always Lie to Strangers* (1951, pp. 95–97) for tales of wild pigeons in the Ozarks. Ben C. Clough (Providence, R.I., *Journal,* June 10, 1951) thinks the story of birds sinking ships may be true, and refers to the Greek tale of Theogenes who was drowned in the Libyan Sea when a flock of tired cranes alighted on his barge. (V.R.)

This belongs under Motif B 878.1, "Giant flocks of birds." (H.H.)

SAM FENTON WAS TEMPTED

Told by Mrs. Elizabeth Maddocks, Joplin, Mo., June, 1937. She heard it recited by a man named Groom, in Taney county,

Mo., about 1907. These dialogues between a native and a traveler are common in backwoods humor. See Opie Read (*Opie Read in the Ozarks,* 1905, pp. 12–17, 22–25, 52–57); J. W. Carr (*Dialect Notes,* III, 1905, 71); also the "Arkansas Traveler" texts in Masterson's *Tall Tales of Arkansaw* (Boston, 1943, pp. 186–219, 361–63. Cf. my *Funny Stories from Arkansas* (1943, p. 21). (V.R.)

For interesting discussion and further examples of such dialogues see Walter Blair, "Inquisitive Yankee Descendants in Arkansas," *American Speech,* XIV (1939), 11–22; Mody C. Boatright, *Folk Laughter on the American Frontier* (New York, 1949), pp. 47–51. For a Tennessee dialogue see Garland (*Tennessee Folklore Society Bulletin,* XXI [1955], 11–13). (H.H.)

PLUMBING IN OKLAHOMA

Told by Mr. Frank Pickett, Eureka Springs, Ark., December, 1951. It is related as a true story, but I believe it is rather widely known in the Southwest. (V.R.)

THREE SILVER LEGS

Told by Mrs. Mary Burke, Springfield, Mo., December, 1935. She had it from relatives in Christian county, Mo., about 1910. Cf. a Negro story reported by Charles van Ravenswaay (*Bulletin of the Missouri Historical Society,* VI, July, 1950, p. 475) from Boonville, Mo.; also *Midwest Folklore,* VI, 1 (Spring, 1956) 39–40. (V.R.)

CAN RATS READ?

Told by Mr. John Chaney, Springfield, Mo., October, 1945. He said it came from Howell county, Mo., in the 1920s. I heard related tales near Sallisaw, Okla., and Pineville, Mo., about 1925. Several residents of Stone county, Mo., mentioned "a letter to the rats" in 1934. Frances Donovan told me that she heard a similar story from Mrs. Katherine Morgan, Eureka Springs, Ark., as recently as 1946. Cf. B. C. Clough (*The American Imagination at*

Work, 1947, pp. 188–93). See *Midwest Folklore,* VI, 1 (Spring, 1956) 43–45. (V.R.)

Botkin (*Treasury of New England Folklore,* pp. 624–27) gives several examples of the letter to rats. (H.H.)

THE PAPER SALESMAN

Told by Mr. Jeff Strong, at Roaring River near Cassville, Mo., April, 1941. He had it from "Watermelon Charley" Smith, of Aurora, Mo. Cf. a similar tale which John F. Dunckel (*The Molly-joggers,* Springfield, Mo., n.d., pp. 15–16) heard in Greene county, Mo., about 1903. (V.R.)

HE TALKED KIND OF SLOW

Told by Mr. T. A. McQuary, Galena, Mo., December, 1935. Cf. my *Funny Stories from Arkansas* (1943, p. 5).

THEM DRUNKEN PAINTERS

Told by Mr. Reggie Courtney, Joplin, Mo., March, 1926. Cf. the news item "Drunken Painters Hit Ozark Farmer" (*Bull Shoals Gazette,* Forsyth, Mo., Sept. 10, 1951), also Bennett Cerf (*Saturday Review of Literature,* Dec. 22, 1951, p. 4). (V.R.)

See Schermerhorn (*Schermerhorn's Stories,* pp. 188–89) for a variant. In an Ohio story in Halpert, *Hoosier Folklore,* VII, 72, an Irishman is warned about passing cars, then is hit by a motorcycle. He says to the man who had warned him, "I didn't know it had a colt." (H.H.)

THE SON OF A BISHOP

Told by a gentleman in Polk county, Ark., April, 1938. Candidates for public office, in the backwoods, are expected to denounce the theory of organic evolution. See a letter from Congressman Brooks Hays (*Arkansas Gazette,* Aug. 5, 1951) about his experience in Baxter county, Ark. As I write these lines it is still against the law to teach evolution at the University of Arkansas. Gerald W. Johnson tells a related tale in "The Compensations of

Deafness" (*Harper's Magazine,* September, 1951, p. 94) which he says is at least thirty years old. (V.R.)

This is a form of Type 1698, "Deaf Persons and their Foolish Answers." In a version with a Republican slant (Anon., *Funny Side Up,* New York, 1952, p. 64), an old lady introduces a new deacon to her deaf husband. Her husband thinks she has said he is a "New Dealer." "No, new *deacon.* He's the son of a bishop." Her husband shakes his head wisely and says, "They all are." (H.H.)

THE MAN THAT HATED BATS

Told by Mr. Frank Payne, Galena, Mo., November, 1932. He apparently regarded it as a true story. J. W. Carr and Rupert Taylor, professors at the University of Arkansas, repeated the old legend (*Dialect Notes,* III, 1909, p. 399). "Once all the bats were confined in Hell. They still have wings like the Devil. One day someone left the gate open, and they quickly darted out and escaped to earth." (V.R.)

GOLD IS WHERE YOU FIND IT

Told by Mr. Farmer Goodwin, Joplin, Mo., February, 1930. He had it from old-timers in Sequoya county, Okla. For a fictionized version of this tale see Barney Blake's "Business Is Business" (*Liberty Magazine,* March 5, 1932, p. 21). Cf. similar items in Botkin (*Treasury of Western Folklore,* 1951, p. 439). (V.R.)

CRUELTY TO ANIMALS

Told by Mr. Frank Payne, Galena, Mo., November, 1932. I have heard many such tales, usually related as news items with names and dates. People near Southwest City, Mo., used to tell of two boys who set a rabbit afire; the rabbit ran under a big hay-barn which burned to the ground. Cf. a reference in the *Missouri Conservationist* (Jefferson City, Mo., April, 1950, p. 11) to a Laclede county farmer who "tied dynamite on a hawk's leg, then saw the roof of his barn blown off." The *Arkansas Gazette* (Oct.

15, 1951) mentions the scoundrels at Mena who "poured oil on a dog's back and then set the dog afire, almost burning down Nabor Shaw's house when the animal crawled through an air vent in the foundation." (V.R.)

This seems related to Motif J 2101.1, "Lighting the cat's tail." In a version from Kashmir given by W. A. Clouston (*The Book of Noodles,* London, 1888, pp. 615–16), a woman, wishing to punish a cat, soaks some cotton wool in oil, and sets it afire after tying it to the cat's tail. The cat climbs to the house roof, ignites the thatch, and sets the house on fire. Eventually the whole village is destroyed by the flames. (H.H.)

YOU AIN'T COMING BACK

Told by Mr. Lon Jordan, Farmington, Ark., November, 1941. He heard it near Fayetteville, Ark., about 1905. Cf. L. B. Williams (*Master Book of Humorous Illustrations,* New York, 1938, p. 315); and Homer Croy (*What Grandpa Laughed At,* 1948, pp. 234–35). (V.R.)

Varying chiefly in length and in the amount offered to the moonshiner's son, this dialogue has been reported from eastern Tennessee by North Callahan (*Smoky Mountain Country,* New York and Boston, 1952, p. 109); from the Ozarks by Rayburn (*Ozark Country,* New York, 1941, p. 344); and from Texas by Botkin (*Treasury of Southern Folklore,* p. 124). Professor Josiah H. Combs has an unpublished text from eastern Kentucky. (H.H.)

THEY PRAYED TO THE SUN

Told by Mr. J. H. McGee, Joplin, Mo., July, 1934. It seems to be widely known in the Southwest as a "legend" attributed to the Cherokees, Choctaws, and Kiowas, with various dates and place-names. Some old Oklahomans say that the fat woman's name was Tanner, and she came out from Washington, D.C., about 1890. W. E. Freeland (*White River Leader,* Branson, Mo., July 11, 1947) repeats the tale, and says that "it happened more than fifty years ago" among the Dakotas. Cf. *Midwest Folklore,* VI, 1 (Spring, 1956) 47–48. (V.R.)

THE CROW THAT TALKED

Told by Dr. L. K. Charles, Eureka Springs, Ark., July, 1948.
He credits it to an old-timer near Berryville, Ark. See Homer Croy
(*What Grandpa Laughed At,* 1948, pp. 46–48) for a related story
of a talking dog, which was popular around Maryville, Mo., in
1897. (V.R.)

Mr. Randolph's tale, and the Missouri variant he notes above,
are the only American versions reported of a tale well-known in
northern Europe. A woman is the victim of the gag in the standard
form. See Type 1750, Motif K 1271.1.3, "Educated chickens tell
of woman's adultery." (H.H.)

JACK AND THE OLD WITCH

Told by Mr. Lon Jordan, Farmington, Ark., October, 1941. He
said it was an old fairy-tale, known to many country children in
the early 1900s. (V.R.)

This is the third version in English of Type 401, "The Princess
Transformed into Deer." Both of the others, Carter (*Journal of
American Folklore,* XXXVIII, 349), and Chase (*Jack Tales,* pp.
127–34), are from North Carolina, and combine Type 401 with
the last part of Type 935, "The Prodigal's Return." (H.H.)

THE DEATH OF LITTLE JEMSON

Told by Dr. Leo McKellops, Anderson, Mo., July, 1933. He
heard it near Steelville, Mo., about 1910. Jemson is a dialect word
for penis. Mr. Jack Short, Galena, Mo., tells me that when he
was a boy, in the 1870s, jemson or jemmison was the common
term, used by everybody. Few of the younger people nowadays
are familiar with it. Perhaps the word derives somehow from
jimsonweed (*Datura stramonium*), a plant said to carry some
esoteric sexual significance. Cf. Randolph and Wilson (*Down in
the Holler,* 1953, p. 100). (V.R.)

SIGNS OF THE TIMES

Told by Mr. Frank Shelton, Eureka Springs, Ark., June, 1951.
Mr. Shelton heard it in Yell county, Ark., in the 1930's. (V.R.)

ICE IN THE BEER

Told by Mr. Jack Short, Galena, Mo., January, 1943. Cf. my *Funny Stories About Hillbillies* (1944, pp. 19–20). (V.R.)

TEDDY KETCHUM

Told by Mr. Franklin Allen, Eureka Springs, Ark., June, 1950. He heard it near Joplin, Mo., in the 1920s. E. H. Mott (*Pike County Folks*, 1883, pp. 37–41) tells a related yarn about the Missouri boy fighting a bear with his axe, while the old man hollers, "Don't spile the skin!" (V.R.)

An almost equal detachment in the outcome of a man's fight with a bear is expressed by a wife in a story quoted by Botkin (*Treasury of New England Folklore*, pp. 146–47, from *Danvis Folks*, by Rowland E. Robinson). She encourages both the man and the bear remarking that "it's the fust fight ever I see 'at I didn't keer which licked." (H.H.)

THE BLOODY MILLER

Told by Mrs. Elizabeth Maddocks, Joplin, Mo., July, 1937. She heard it in Christian county, Mo., about 1900, and regarded it as a true story. The tale may be related to a song "Donderback's Machine" (Spaeth, *Read 'Em and Weep*, 1927, p. 90). See my *Ozark Folksongs* (III, 1949, pp. 253–54) for texts of the song collected in Missouri and Arkansas. J. C. Edwards of Webster Grove, Mo. (*Arkansas Folklore*, II, May, 1952, p. 8), tells a similar story about the cannibal Dunderbeck who made sausage of his neighbor's children, and was finally ground up in his own machine. The "Silver Dick" mentioned in Mrs. Maddocks' tale is Richard Parks Bland, a free-silver congressman from Lebanon, Mo., who came near getting the Democratic nomination for President in 1896. (V.R.)

Boggs (*Journal of American Folklore*, XLVII, 298) gives a North Carolina story about human flesh eaters, and remarks it is "an example of the innumerable descriptions of ghastly situations so popular among American storytellers." (H.H.)

THE SHERIFF GIVE HIM ROPE

Told by Mr. Ed Worden, Eureka Springs, Ark., October, 1948.
He said it dated to the 1890s. Cf. George W. Peck (*Sunbeams,*
Chicago, 1910, pp. 22–24). (V.R.)

DUNWOODY'S LAST JOKE

Told by Mrs. Marie Wilbur, Pineville, Mo., March, 1930. She
had it from Dr. O. St. John, also of Pineville, in the 1920s. He did
not regard it as a true story, but probably an old minstrel-show
joke. See *Midwest Folklore,* VI, 1 (Spring, 1956) 48–49. (V.R.)

RIDING ON THE CARS

Told by Mr. Wythe Bishop, Fayetteville, Ark., December, 1941.
Cf. Press Woodruff (*A Backwoods Philosopher from Arkansaw,*
Chicago, 1901, pp. 255–57); also Dreamy Bill (*The Arkansaw I
Saw,* 1919, pp. 51–53). (V.R.)

THE BELLED BUZZARD

Told by Mr. E. J. Ferris, Little Rock, Ark., December, 1927.
There are many stories of belled buzzards in the Ozarks. See Ed-
win W. Mills (*Missouri Magazine,* IX, 11 [May, 1937], p. 8);
Ford (*Traditional Music of America,* 1940, pp. 187–88); Botkin
(*Treasury of Southern Folklore,* 1949, pp. 474–75; Rayburn
(*Ozark Guide* [Spring, 1950], pp. 68–69). May Kennedy McCord
(KWTO, Springfield, Mo., May 21, 1950) broadcast several of
these tales, including one about a buzzard in a red flannel shirt.
Cf. the account in my *We Always Lie to Strangers* (1951, pp.
260–61). Ralph Pogue (Noel, Mo., *Press,* Aug. 17, 1951) prints
reports of belled buzzards from nine different localities in Mis-
souri and Arkansas. Some old settlers believe that buzzards seek
out and vomit upon men guilty of incest; see my *From an Ozark
Holler* (1933, p. 92) and *Ozark Superstitions* (1947, p. 245).
Fred High (*It Happened in the Ozarks,* 1954, p. 51) says that a

preacher near Oak Grove, Ark., really did hear a belled buzzard, and thought God was sending an angel after him. (V.R.)

A LITTLE PIECE OE THREAD

Told by Mrs. Louise Platt Hauck, St. Joseph, Mo., July, 1932. She had it from old settlers in Barry county, Mo. (V.R.)

See Williams (*Master Book of Humorous Illustrations,* p. 191) for a text of this story. (H.H.)

THE BIG RABBITS

Told by Mr. Rex Thomas, Lamar, Mo., November, 1934. He had it from Jack Coleman, who lived near Milford, Mo. Jackrabbits are not uncommon in western Missouri and Arkansas today, but old residents say they were rare before 1900. Cf. my *We Always Lie to Strangers* (1951, p. 263), also a legend about the origin of the Missouri mule reported by Don Pryor (Springfield, Mo., *News,* Jan. 29, 1952). (V.R.)

HOW TO GET RID OF DOCTORS

Told by Mr. Marcus Freck, Beardstown, Ill., August, 1925. He heard it near Hot Springs, Ark., about 1899. (V.R.)

THE PREACHER WOULDN'T EAT

Told by Mr. Joe Ingenthron, Forsyth, Mo., June, 1940. May Kennedy McCord (Springfield, Mo., *Leader & Press,* June 10, 1934) credits the story to Charles Henson of Galena, Mo. Cf. L. B. Williams (*Master Book of Humorous Illustrations,* New York, 1938, pp. 258–59). (V.R.)

This is probably a standard joke about preachers although I know only a few published references. For a New England version see Botkin (*Treasury of New England Folklore,* p. 188). Allan M. Trout gave a Kentucky version in his column, "Greetings," Louisville *Courier-Journal,* October 10, 1951, and I have an unpublished Kentucky text in my folklore archive. The story is particularly ironical because in folk tradition preachers are notoriously hearty eaters. (H.H.)

THREE FOOT DEEPER

Told by Mr. Clyde Harris, Tar River, Okla., July, 1927. He said that it was a common story around Joplin, Mo., in the early days. (V.R.)

Hand (*California Folklore Quarterly,* I [1942], 37–39) discusses California versions of the legend of the mines in which a strike was made on the very last round shot. He says "there are numerous humorous accounts of firm resolves to blast one more round" and gives (p. 39) a variant of Mr. Randolph's yarn. In the Texas oil fields Boatright (*Publications of the Texas Folklore Society,* XXV, 83–84) reports legends of oil wells struck because orders to quit drilling were not relayed to the drillers for several hours. In that interval oil was struck. (H.H.)

THE NECESSITIES OF LIFE

Told by Dr. Leo McKellops, Anderson, Mo., May, 1933. Old-timers declare that the story goes back at least to the 1880s. I heard it in a Little Rock, Ark., saloon about 1913. Bob Burns and his imitators used it in the early 1930s, and O. O. McIntyre (syndicated column, Dec. 16, 1935) said that it "cracked the serenity of a Tory group of thumb-twiddlers at the Union League recently." I published the yarn myself (*University Review,* Kansas City, Mo. [Spring, 1937], pp. 180–81) with references to Burns and McIntyre. Cf. L. B. Williams (*Master Book of Humorous Illustrations,* New York, 1938, p. 278), also my *Funny Stories About Hillbillies* (1944, p. 3). (V.R.)

Masterson (*Tall Tales of Arkansaw,* p. 179) gives a version of this. Professor Josiah H. Combs has a variant in an unpublished manuscript of tales from the mountains of east Kentucky. (H.H.)

RIDDLE ME THIS

Told by Mr. Pete Woolsey, Pineville, Mo., September, 1924. He had it from a farmer in Benton county, Ark. The same story appears in Williams (*Master Book of Humorous Illustrations,* 1938, p. 317). The old settlers say that conundrums and catch questions were enormously popular in the early days. Not many of these items are remembered now, but Isabel Spradley and I published some Ozark riddles (*Journal of American Folklore,* 47 [1934], pp. 81–89), and I collaborated with Archer Taylor in a similar paper (*Southern Folklore Quarterly,* 8 [1944], pp. 1–10). Cf. my *Funny Stories About Hillbillies* (1944, p. 9). (V.R.)

THE MAN FROM TEXAS

Told by Mr. J. L. Russell, Harrison, Ark., April, 1950. My informants say that these gags were old in the 1870s, but they are still being printed in the Ozark newspapers. For recent examples see the Harrison, Ark., *Times* (March 5, 1951), the *Bull Shoals Gazette* (Forsyth, Mo., Sept. 12, 1951), and the *Arkansas Gazette* (Little Rock, Ark., Dec. 15, 1951). (V.R.)

In Williams (*Master Book of Humorous Illustrations,* p. 188) it is a Los Angeles man who is told he can enter heaven "but won't like it." There are many other "heaven's gate" stories about Texans. (H.H.)

A BARREL OF POPCORN

Told by Mr. Frank Pickett, Eureka Springs, Ark., March, 1952. It really happened, he says, not far from Joplin, Mo. I have heard several versions, with different names and settings, but am unable to locate the story in print. (V.R.)

CHANGE THE NAME OF ARKANSAS?

Told by Mr. Farwell Gould, Pittsburg, Kan., July, 1929. He never saw it in print, but had a manuscript copy of "Senator Johnson's speech" obtained in Kansas City, Mo., dated 1899. Mr. Gould says it was often delivered by "actors and comedians at stag suppers, in saloons and places like that." This item has been famous for many years, but little is known of its provenience. Marquis James (*The Cherokee Strip,* 1945, p. 282) heard it in Oklahoma about 1910. Old settlers tell me that it was recited in

215

Arkansas before 1890. Cf. C. L. Edson (*Nation,* CXVI [May 2, 1923], p. 516); Fred Allsopp (*Folklore of Romantic Arkansas,* 1931, II, pp. 87–89); Travis Y. Oliver (*Vanity Fair,* XLI [September, 1933], p. 57); Hal Norwood (*Just a Book,* Mena, Ark., 1938, pp. 26–27); and Avantus Green (*With This We Challenge,* Little Rock, Ark., 1945, p. 4). For unexpurgated texts see Masterson (*Tall Tales of Arkansaw,* 1943, pp. 353–54). John Gould Fletcher (*Arkansas,* 1947, p. vii) says that the pronunciation of the word Arkansas "has given rise to a folk tale of considerable grossness." The Arkansas legislature (March, 1881) affirmed that the name should be pronounced "Arkansaw," with the accent on the first syllable. But Dallas T. Herndon, of the Arkansas History Commission, finds no reference to Senator Cassius M. Johnson's great speech in the official records. The Arkansawyers have not forgotten, however. As recently as January 12, 1953, an editorial in the *Arkansas Gazette* concluded, "There is still danger that someone with an eye canted to the northwest of us might again try to change the name of Arkansas." (V.R.)

JOHNNY'S LITTLE DOG

Told by Mrs. Linnie Bullard, Pineville, Mo., July, 1926. Cf. Press Woodruff (*A Backwoods Philosopher from Arkansaw,* Chicago, 1901, p. 290); and Marion Hughes (*Three Years in Arkansaw,* 1904, pp. 32–33). (V.R.)

THERE'S A SLEIGHT TO IT

Told by Mr. A. L. Cline, Joplin, Mo., July, 1922. He heard it in Benton county, Ark., about 1895. (V.R.)

Botkin (*Treasury of New England Folklore,* p. 197) gives two New England stories in each of which a man gives a breakdown of his charge for doing a certain job: the smaller part is for the actual labor, the larger for knowing how. In a New York story given by Thompson (*Body, Boot & Britches,* p. 167) a woodcutter balances his labor against the work done by a lawyer who had collected a bill for him. He cuts wood for the lawyer for almost an hour, then tells the lawyer, "Well, boss, I've worked as long as you did; so we will call it quits." (H.H.)

ON TRIAL FOR HIS LIFE

Told by a lawyer in Jefferson City, Mo., February, 1935. He had it from Colonel R. C. Ford, Forsyth, Mo., in the 1920s. A similar tale is credited to Mr. Jesse Tolerton, also of Forsyth. (V.R.)

It is an assault trial, a shorter distance, and "some confounded fool" in the version in Brown (*Wit and Humor*, Chicago, 1880, pp. 55–56). See also Hazlitt (*Joe Miller in Motley*, London & New York, 1892, p. 51). (H.H.)

WOLVES ARE MY BROTHERS

Told by Mr. Ed Wall, Pineville, Mo., April, 1922. He heard it from a trapper who lived near Rutledge, Mo., in the early days. (V.R.)

Cf. Motifs B 314, "Helpful animal brothers-in-law," and B 453.3, "Helpful wolf" in the revised edition of Thompson (*Motif-Index of Folk-Literature*, Bloomington, 1955, vol. 1). (H.H.)

OLD HORNY

Told by Mr. J. H. Storey, Pineville, Mo., July, 1922. He came from Pea Ridge, Ark., where he heard the story as a child. Cf. Raymond Weeks (*The Hound-Tuner of Callaway*, 1927, pp. 1–29). Burning bodies on driftwood is not uncommon in the Ozarks; an unidentified body was so cremated near Forsyth, Mo. (Springfield, Mo. *Press*, June 8, 1931). See also the "Ringtail Tooter" story by Joe and Frank Wig (*Ree-Laxin' at Skranky Knob*, Hannibal, Mo., 1948, pp. 51–58) about a dog that learned to whistle like a locomotive. (V.R.)

SHE WANTED A DIVORCE

Told by a lady at Branson, Mo., September, 1941. She had it from a farmer near Walnut Shade, Mo., about 1900. Cf. Joey Adams (*From Gags to Riches*, New York, 1949, p. 52). (V.R.)

BACKHOUSE ALBERT'S MONEY

Told by Mr. Martin Travis, Joplin, Mo., January, 1927. He got it near Southwest City, Mo., about 1905. (V.R.)

Stories on tight-fisted characters are popular in the American folk tradition. For two variants of this story, see Williams (*Master Book of Humorous Illustrations,* pp. 143 and 292). In a Grayson county, Kentucky, yarn given in Allan M. Trout's "Greetings," Louisville *Courier-Journal,* June 8, 1954, a frugal wagon driver remarks that in all his life he had spent only ten cents foolishly. One day he forgot to take his lunch and had to buy a dime's worth of cheese and crackers. (H.H.)

THE CAT'S FOOT

Told by Mr. Lon Jordon, Farmington, Ark., December, 1941. Compare a related tale reported from the Ozarks by Charles Morrow Wilson (*Folk-Say,* Norman, Okla., 1930, p. 167). I collected several versions of this tale in the late 1920s. One of them was published in *Folk-Say* (1931, pp. 90–91), and reprinted in *Ozark Mountain Folks* (1932, pp. 36–38). Cf. my *Ozark Superstitions* (1947, p. 269); also Collins (*Legends and Lore of Missouri,* 1951, p. 13). (V.R.)

This tale is Motif G 252, "Witch in form of cat has hand cut off"; also D 702.1.1, "Cat's paw cut off: woman's hand missing." E. E. Gardner (*Folklore from the Schoharie Hills, New York,* Ann Arbor, 1937, p. 74) gives a New York text and, in note 139, a long list of European and American references. To an Indiana text which I published in *Hoosier Folklore Bulletin* I, 60–61, I added references to supplement Gardner. Many more references could be added to demonstrate the great popularity of this story. Since it is clearly a tale of international distribution, it should be included in the expected revision of Aarne and Thompson's *The Types of the Folk-Tale.* (H.H.)

LITTLE TOODY

Told by Mrs. Marie Wilbur, Pineville, Mo., March, 1930. She had it from a woman near Searcy, Ark. Cf. Allsopp (*Folklore of Romantic Arkansas,* 1931, II, pp. 169–70). (V.R.)

Although this story echoes parts of several international tales, motivation for the girl's transformation into a stone is curiously

218

lacking. Wc have here Motif N 831.1, "Mysterious housekeeper," and, for the liaison, T 110, "Marriage of mortal and supernatural being." (H.H.)

ADAM AND EVE

Told by a gentleman who must remain anonymous, Siloam Springs, Ark., July, 1949. He insists that it is a true story, from Newton county, Ark. (V.R.)

For a variant see Williams (*Master Book of Humorous Illustrations,* p. 14). (H.H.)

BIBLIOGRAPHY OF
WORKS CITED

Aarne, Antti, and Stith Thompson. The Types of the Folk-Tale. Helsinki, 1928. Folklore Fellows Communications, No. 74. Cited as Type.

Adams, Joey. From Gags to Riches. New York, 1949.

Addy, Sidney Oldall. Household Tales with Other Traditional Remains. London and Sheffield, 1895.

Allen, J. C. Tales and Trails of Martha's Vineyard. Boston, 1938.

Allsopp, Fred W. Folklore of Romantic Arkansas. 2 vols. New York, 1931.

Anderson, Walter. Kaiser und Abt. Helsinki, 1923. Folklore Fellows Communications, No. 42.

Anecdota Americana. New York, 1934.

Baughman, Ernest W. A Comparative Study of the Folktales of England and North America. 3 vols. Indiana University doctoral dissertation, 1953.

Bett, Henry. English Legends. 2d ed. London and New York, 1952.

Blakeborough, R. Wit, Character, Folklore and Customs of the North Riding of Yorkshire. London, 1898.

Boatright, Mody C. Folk Laughter on the American Frontier. New York, 1949.

Botkin, B. A. Lay My Burden Down. Chicago, 1945.

—— Treasury of American Folklore. New York, 1944.

—— Treasury of New England Folklore. New York, 1947.

—— Treasury of Southern Folklore. New York, 1949.

—— Treasury of Western Folklore. New York, 1951.

Bradley, W. O. Stories and Speeches of William O. Bradley. Lexington, Kentucky, 1916.

Brown, Marshall. Wit and Humor. Chicago, 1880.

Callahan, North. Smoky Mountain Country. New York and Boston, 1952.

Campbell, J. F. Popular Tales of the West Highlands. 4 vols. Edinburgh, 1860–62.

Carrière, Joseph. Tales from the French Folklore of Missouri. Evanston, Ill., 1937.

Carson, Charles. Mountain Troubadour. Los Angeles, 1951.

Cerf, Bennett. Anything for a Laugh. New York, 1946.

Chambers, Robert. Popular Rhymes of Scotland. London and Edinburgh, 1870.

Chandler, F. W. The Literature of Roguery. 2 vols. Boston and New York, 1907.

Chase, Richard. The Jack Tales. Cambridge, 1943.

Child, Francis J. The English and Scottish Popular Ballads. 5 vols. Boston and New York, 1882–1898.

Clough, Ben C. The American Imagination at Work. New York, 1947.

Clouston, W. A. The Book of Noodles. London, 1888.

—— Popular Tales and Fictions. 2 vols. Edinburgh and London, 1887.

Collins, E. A. Legends and Lore of Missouri. San Antonio, 1951.

Courlander, Harold and G. Herzog. The Cow-Tail Switch. New York, 1947.

Croy, Homer. What Grandpa Laughed At. New York, 1948.

Dorson, Richard M. Negro Folktales in Michigan. Cambridge, 1956.

Dreamy Bill. The Arkansaw I Saw. Baltimore, 1919.

Dunckel, John F. The Mollyjoggers. Springfield, Mo., c. 1908.

Eberhard, W. Chinese Fairy Tales and Folk Tales. London, 1937.

Edwards, E. E. Bamboo, Lotus and Palm. London, 1948.

Elgart, J. M. Over Sixteen. New York, 1951.

Emrich, Marion Vallat, and George Korson. The Child's Book of Folklore. New York, 1947.

Evans, Joe M. A Corral Full of Stories. El Paso, Texas, 1939.

Fauset, Arthur Huff. Folklore from Nova Scotia. New York, 1931. Memoirs of the American Folklore Society, Vol. XXIV.

Fletcher, John Gould. Arkansas. Chapel Hill, N.C., 1947.

Ford, Ira W. Traditional Music of America. New York, 1940.

Ford, Robert. Thistledown: A Book of Scotch Humour, Character, Folk-Lore, Story and Anecdote. New York, 1891.

Frobenius, Leo, and D. C. Fox. African Genesis. New York, 1937.

Funny Side Up. New York, 1952.

Gardner, Emelyn E. Folklore from the Schoharie Hills, New York. Ann Arbor, Mich., 1937.

Ginzberg, Louis. The Legends of the Jews. 7 vols. Philadelphia, 1909–38.

Graham, Jean. Tales of the Osage River Country. Clinton, Mo., 1929.

Green, Avantus. With This We Challenge. Little Rock, Ark., 1945.

Gutch, Eliza, and Mabel Peacock. Examples of Printed Folklore Concerning Lincolnshire. London, 1908. Publications of the Folk-Lore Society, Vol. LXVIII.

Harlin, Amos. For Here Is My Fortune. New York, 1946.

Hazlitt, W. Carew. Joe Miller in Motley. London and New York, 1892.

—— New London Jest Book. London, 1871.

—— Studies in Jocular Literature. New York, 1890.

Herndon, Dallas T. Centennial History of Arkansas. 3 vols. Chicago and Little Rock. 1922.

High, Fred. Forty-Three Years for Uncle Sam. Berryville, Ark., 1949.

—— It Happened in the Ozarks. Berryville, Ark., 1954.

Hoenshal, E. J., and L. S. Hoenshel. Stories of the Pioneers. Branson, Mo., 1915.

Hogue, Wayman. Back Yonder. New York, 1932.

Hole, Christina. English Folklore. 2d ed. London, 1945.

Hughes, Marion. Three Years in Arkansaw. Chicago, 1904.

Hurston, Zora Neale. Mules and Men. Philadelphia, 1935.

Idaho, a Guide in Word and Picture. Federal Writers' Project, Caldwell, Idaho, 1937.

Jackson, Thomas W. On a Slow Train through Arkansas. Chicago, 1903.

Jacobs, Joseph. English Fairy Tales. 2d ed. New York and London, 1893.

—— More English Fairy Tales. London, 1894.

James, Marquis. The Cherokee Strip. New York, 1945.

Jones, W. H., and L. L. Kropf. The Folk-Tales of the Magyars. London, 1889.

Joyce, P. W. Old Irish Folk Music and Songs. New York and Dublin, 1909.

Kennedy, Patrick. Legendary Fictions of the Irish Celts. London and New York, 1891.

Kim So-Un. The Story Bag: A Collection of Korean Folk Tales. Rutland, Vt., and Tokyo, Japan, c. 1955.

Korson, George. Minstrels of the Mine Patch. Philadelphia, 1938.

Leather, Ella M. The Folk-Lore of Herefordshire. Hereford and London, 1912.

Lewis, E. C. After Dinner Stories. New York and Boston, 1905.

Lockridge, Norman. Waggish Tales of the Czechs. Chicago, 1947.

Lurie, Charles N. Make 'Em Laugh: Humorous Stories for All Occasions. New York, 1927.

MacGregor, A. A. The Peat-Fire Flame: Folk-Tales and Traditions of the Highlands and Islands. Edinburgh and London, 1947.

Mackensen, Lutz. Der singende Knochen. Helsinki, 1923. Folklore Fellows Communications, No. 49.

Manson, W. L. The Highland Bagpipe, Its History, Literature and Music. Paisley and London, 1901.

Masterson, James R. Tall Tales of Arkansaw. Boston, 1943.

Mirandy (pseud.). Breezes from Persimmon Holler. Hollywood, Calif., 1943.

Mott, E. H. Pike County Folks. New York, 1883.

Norwood, Hal. Just a Book. Mena, Ark., 1938.

Ó Súilleabháin, Seán. A Handbook of Irish Folklore. Dublin, 1942.

Owen, Mary Alicia. Voodoo Tales. New York and London, 1893.

Ozark Guide. Ed. by Otto Ernest Rayburn, Eureka Springs, Ark.,

1943 —. Several issues of this quarterly magazine are cited in the notes.

Palmer, P. M., and R. P. More. Sources of the Faust Tradition. New York, 1936.

Parsons, Elsie Clews. Folklore from the Cape Verde Islands. 2 vols. Cambridge and New York, 1923. Memoirs of the American Folklore Society, Vol. XV.

—— Folklore of the Antilles, French and English. 3 vols. New York, 1933, 1936, 1943. Memoirs of the American Folklore Society, Vol. XXVI. Cited as Parsons, *Antilles*.

—— Folklore of the Sea Islands, South Carolina. Cambridge and New York, 1923. Memoirs of the American Folklore Society, Vol. XVI.

Peck, George W. Sunbeams. Chicago, 1910.

Percy, William A. Lanterns on the Levee. New York, 1941.

Pratt, Otho. Gensang Jones' Ozark Tales. Verona, Mo., 1951.

Randolph, Vance. The Devil's Pretty Daughter. New York, 1955.

—— From an Ozark Holler. New York, 1933.

—— Funny Stories About Hillbillies. Girard, Kan., 1944.

—— Funny Stories from Arkansas. Girard, Kan., 1943.

—— Ozark Folksongs. 4 vols. Columbia, Mo., 1946–1950.

—— Ozark Ghost Stories. Girard, Kan., 1944.

—— Ozark Mountain Folks. New York, 1932.

—— Ozark Superstitions. New York, 1947.

—— We Always Lie to Strangers. New York, 1951.

—— Who Blowed Up the Church House? New York, 1952.

Randolph, Vance, and George P. Wilson. Down in the Holler, a Gallery of Ozark Folk Speech. Norman, Okla., 1953.

Rayburn, Otto Ernest. Ozark Country. New York, 1941.

Read, Opie. Opie Read in the Ozarks. Chicago, 1905.

Roberts, Leonard W. South from Hell-fer-Sartin. Lexington, Kentucky, 1955.

Robinson, Rowland E. Danvis Folks. Boston and New York, 1894.

Saxon, Lyle, and others. Gumbo Ya-Ya. Boston, 1945.

Schermerhorn, James. Schermerhorn's Stories. New York, 1928.

Seymour, St. John D. Tales of King Solomon. London, 1924.

Shackleford, William Yancey. Gun-Fighters of the Old West. Girard, Kan., 1943.

Shaw, M. F. Folksongs and Folklore of South Uist. London, 1955.

Simpkins, J. E. Examples of Printed Folklore Concerning Fife. London, 1914.

Smith, H. Allen. The Compleat Practical Joker. New York, 1953.

Spaeth, Sigmund. Read 'Em and Weep. Garden City, N.Y., 1927.

Spalding, Mattingly. Bardstown, Town of Tradition. Baltimore, 1942.

Spofford, A. R. Library of Wit and Humor. 4 vols. Philadelphia, 1899.

Spurlock, Pearl. Over the Old Ozark Trails. Branson, Mo., 1936.

Sturges, J. A. History of McDonald County, Missouri. Pineville, Mo., 1897.

Thompson, Harold W. Body, Boots and Britches. Philadelphia, 1940.

Thompson, Stith. The Folktale. New York, 1946.

—— Motif-Index of Folk-Literature. 6 vols. Bloomington, Ind., 1932–1936. Cited as Motif.

Thorp, N. Howard, and Neil M. Clark. Pardner of the Wind. Caldwell, Idaho, 1945.

Vincent, Bert. Here in Tennessee. Knoxville, Tenn., 1945.

Weeks, Raymond. The Hound-Tuner of Callaway. New York, 1927.

Wig, Joe, and Frank Wig. Ree-laxin' at Skranky Knob. Hannibal, Mo., 1948.

Williams, L. B. Master Book of Humorous Illustrations. New York and Nashville, Tenn., 1938.

Woodruff, Press. A Backwoods Philosopher from Arkansaw. Chicago, 1901.

Zinsser, Hans. As I Remember Him. Boston, 1940.

266   120